FOUNDATIONS OF
IMMUNOCHEMISTRY

FOUNDATIONS OF
IMMUNOCHEMISTRY

Eugene D. Day, Ph.D.

Professor of Immunology
and
Director of Graduate Studies
Department of Microbiology and Immunology
School of Medicine
Duke University
Durham, North Carolina

The Williams & Wilkins Company / Baltimore • 1966

With love to Mother and Dad

Preface

The historical development of immunochemistry as a science would appear to the casual observer to display a reverse in the order of sequences that ought to characterize a scientific discipline, if development were to be logical. Stemming from the larger field of immunology, the subject of immunochemistry has for many years loosely bound together a variety of techniques and concepts that have developed with surprising disunity and singularity. Many immunochemical techniques had been pragmatically devised, polished with near infinite detail, and clearly relegated as separate entities to the field of art long before the unifying thread of theory, which was needed to tie them together, was even spun. Adequate theory has now been produced, and, in the minds of experienced immunochemists, has already begun to unify immunochemistry into an acceptable discipline.[1]

To those of us who find ourselves upon the fringes of basic immunochemical research, however, the science of immunochemistry has remained too disorganized to attract us fully to its whole being. To such scientists, who, like myself, have put off becoming disciplined in the subject, as well as to fully established immunochemists, who would like to view their subject from the grandstand rather than the circus ring, *Foundations of Immunochemistry* is directed, the hope being that with our combined interest and influence Immunochemistry will soon take its deserved place within the formal organization of science.

Svante Arrhenius (1859–1927) coined the term "immunochemistry" in 1904 during a lectureship at the University of California at Berkeley. Better known for his theory of electrolytic dissociation in 1887 and as

---

[1] A footnote to the seemingly illogical development of the science of immunochemistry calls attention to the historical development of other sciences. Upon close scrutiny one may observe that their growth was also, more often than not, "illogical." Thus, although thermodynamics was well developed in its separate parts by the middle of the 19th century, it was not unified and made whole until J. Willard Gibbs published his monograph, "The Equilibrium of Heterogeneous Substances," many years later. Gibbs spun his own unifying thread, making him tall among scientists, whereas the author need only borrow from the many theoreticians of immunochemistry who have already spun many threads. The effect, however, would hopefully be the same: to stimulate new thought, new disunity, new growth, and new theory.

Nobel Prize winner in 1903, the Swedish chemist published his Berkeley lectures under the title *Immunochemistry* (Arrhenius, 1907) with the following prefatory remarks:

> I have given to these lectures the title "Immuno-chemistry," and wish with this word to indicate that the chemical reactions of substances that are produced by the injection of foreign substances into the blood of animals, *i.e.* by immunisation, are under discussion in these pages. From this it follows also—that that the substances with which these products react, as proteins and ferments, are to be here considered with respect to their chemical properties.

In spite of this early formalization of immunochemistry, its subject matter remained a rather esoteric and often unrecognized subdivision of immunology. Monographs on the subject appeared with regularity, beginning with Wells' *The Chemical Aspects of Immunity* (1929) and followed by Landsteiner's *Specificity of Serological Reactions* (1936) and Marrack's *The Chemistry of Antigens and Antibodies* (1938), but it was not until Kabat and Mayer's *Experimental Immunochemistry* appeared (1948) that it really became a full-fledged discipline. Notwithstanding the inclusion of immunochemistry as a formal topic in *Annual Reviews of Biochemistry* at its inception (Heidelberger, 1932), it remained unrecognized as such by *Chemical Abstracts* until 1962 (Volume 56), when the subject was belatedly awarded a section of its own. If a special journal devoted to a particular subject can be used as an indicator of final formalization of that subject, one would judge that immunochemistry did not reach adulthood until April 1964, when an international journal of that name finally made its appearance.

With adulthood comes increasing responsibility and a need to be less self-centered. It was very appropriate, therefore, that the first research paper chosen to begin Volume 1, Number 1, of *Immunochemistry* should be the work of a postdoctoral fellow, and that it should concern itself not with immunochemistry *per se* but with conformational changes that took place within an enzymatically inactive pro-enzyme protein as it was converted to an enzymatically active protein (Gerstein *et al.*, 1964).

At least three approaches are open to teaching a particular science. One way begins with particular reactions that are observed in the laboratory, describes these reactions in detail, constructively criticizes and compares them, and out of the construct speculates about why they occurred as they did. During the early growth of a new science this approach is the only safe one to take. Another begins with laws and formulas and their attendant models or mathematical expressions, develops them for ideal situations, and then inserts modifications to fit what actually is observed in the laboratory. For an established science this approach is conventional.

The third approach begins somewhere in the middle of the other two, and characterizes the teaching of a science for which the principles of reactions are known but where the speculative stage is not mature enough to free the science from the laboratory bench. Whereas the first method of teaching is descriptive and the second is theoretical, the third is essentially analytical. It is along this third avenue that the following chapters lead.

Analytical science begins with the principal reagent it employs: its occurrence in nature, physical and chemical constitution, and the specific qualities it possesses that make it a reagent. Part One, on the structure of antibodies, endeavors to cover these points and to introduce the antibody as the principal type of reagent for the study of immunochemistry.

In any analytical work, the principal reagent requires further analysis in order to be understood adequately. Primary standards, reactive with the reagent, must be used in order to define the useful limits and purity of the reagent. If the subject is oxidation and the reagent is iodine, the reagent is first analyzed in terms of a primary standard of arsenious oxide before its action in a general iodimetric process with unknown reducing agents is undertaken. In the case of immunochemistry, known antigens, particularly specific chemical haptens, purified natural products, and synthetic polymers, can be viewed as primary standards for studying the nature and reactivity of antibodies. Thus, in Part Two the analysis of antibodies in terms of their reactions with known antigens is presented in a number of different ways. After this systematic approach the investigator should be better prepared to study the varied ways in which the principal reagent, antibody, can be used to capture the variety of unknowns that exist in various forms and states. With the principles of reagent reactivity in mind, he can better comprehend and more critically evaluate the many procedures described in the expanding immunochemical literture and in his own laboratory.

Immunochemistry is no different from general analytical chemistry in possessing both qualitative and quantitative sides. Inherent in all analytics is the question of quantitative limits beyond which qualitative analysis for specificity or uniqueness cannot be taken, and so it is in immunochemistry where the question of specificity is always prime. It is not surprising, therefore, that the general aspects of specificity and cross-reactivity should permeate much of the ensuing discussion.

A number of highly specialized techniques are available to the analytical immunochemist for the analysis of unknowns in addition to those discussed herein:

Complement-fixation
Agar-gel double diffusion
Immunoelectrophoresis
Indirect agglutinations
Conglutination
Fluorescent-antibody fixation
Hemagglutination inhibition
Antiglobulin consumption
Radioantibody absorption
Radioantigen precipitation
Immunofiltration
Antibody radioautography
Antibody electron microscopy

It could hardly be the function of the present volume to describe the particular art associated with any one of these or a multitude of others not listed. Fortunately, the number of monographs, symposia, progress reports, and reviews, as well as original papers, has kept pace with demands from the laboratory bench for practical recipes and the theory behind each specialty. Some instrument manufacturers, in fact, are beginning to supply reprints of pertinent work with their apparatus as a part of the package [e.g., O. Ouchterlony's fundamental review, "Diffusion-in-gel Methods for Immunological Analysis. II" (Prog. Allergy 6: 30–154, 1962, with 1185 references), that accompanies a gel-diffusion kit].

Too often taken for granted, or left undiscussed because of lack of time and space, is the nature of the immunological reactions that form the common basis for these techniques. It is hoped that the following chapters will in some measure fill this gap in the burgeoning literature on analytical immunochemistry.

E.D.D.
October 8, 1965

REFERENCES

Arrhenius, S. (1907). *Immunochemistry*, Macmillan (New York, 309 pp.).

Gerstein, J. F., Levine, L., and Van Vunakis, H. (1964). Altered antigenicity of pepsinogen and pepsin as an index of conformational change: effect of urea and reducing agents. Immunochemistry 1:3–14.

Gibbs, J. W. (1876). The equilibrium of heterogeneous substances. Trans. Connecticut Acad. Sci., Vol. 3.

Heidelberger, M. (1932). Immunochemistry. Ann. Rev. Biochem. 1:655–674.

Kabat, E. A., and Mayer, M. M. (1948). *Experimental Immunochemistry*, Charles C Thomas. (Springfield, Ill., 567 pp.). (A second edition, 905 pp., was published in 1961.)

Landsteiner, K. (1936). *Specificity of Serological Reactions*. Charles C Thomas. (Springfield, Ill., 178 pp.).

Marrack, J. R. (1938). *The Chemistry of Antigens and Antibodies*, His Majesty's Stationery Office (London, 194 pp.).

Wells, H. G. (1929). *The Chemical Aspects of Immunity*, Chemical Catalog Co. (New York, 286 pp.).

Acknowledgments

I should like to thank Mrs. Gloria Kearney for her faithful and diligent work as typist, bibliographer, and proof-reader; Mr. James L. Sangston, for his helpful aid and patient understanding as Editor of The Williams & Wilkins Company; the many publishers and authors, cited separately in text and references, for their generous permission to include copyrighted material in these pages, and Mmes. Jane Mahaley and Jo Eiring and Messrs. Sylvester Lassiter, Richard Dennis, and Lewis Rigsbee for their efficient laboratory work while I was writing.

E.D.D.

Contents

PART ONE *Structure of Antibodies*

1

A Word about Proteins and Biological Variescence

In 1907 a joint committee of the American Society of Biological Chemists and the American Physiological Society (J. Biol. Chem. *4:* 48–51, 1908) recommended that proteins be classified according to their solubility, heat coagulability, and hydrolytic derivatives. The classification recognized three groups: simple, conjugated, and derived. Proteins were classed as simple if, upon acid hydrolysis, only amino acids or their derivatives were obtained. Among the simple proteins were albumins and globulins, such as those found in dilute salt solution in serum. These were distinguished from each other by water solubility—the albumins defined as water soluble, the globulins as water insoluble.

It has been clear for about as many years as the classification is old that it is quite inadequate and inaccurate. For example, the term *pseudoglobulin* was coined almost as if to deprecate the nature of a perfectly *bona fide* member of the globulin family just because it was found to be water-soluble. The term *euglobulin*, on the other hand, with its high and lofty prefix, was reserved for the ASBC-APS type of water-insoluble globulin. Even this arrangement was not satisfactory, forcing Kendall (1937), for example, to utilize such terms as water-soluble euglobulins and water-insoluble pseudoglobulins to account for further discrepancies. He had found that two different human serum globulins, when separate, were water-soluble whereas, when mixed, they behaved like a single classical water-insoluble euglobulin. Likewise, nearly all plasma proteins, including the albumins and globulins, have long been known to contain residues of carbohydrate, so much so that Schultze (1962) has reclassified them according to their relative carbohydrate content and their solubility in 0.6 M perchloric acid. In spite of such inadequacies in the ASBC-APS classification of 1907, some relatively modern textbooks of biochemistry persist in introducing proteins to the student on this basis.

One must distinguish between operational and definitive classifications. In the former, a method or procedure reproducibly distinguishes groups of things from each other if even in an arbitrary manner, and is extremely valuable at the analytical stage of development of a particular science. This is evidenced in Chapter 2, where electrophoretic, ultracentrifugal, diffusion, solubility, immunoelectrophoretic, chromatographic, ion-exchange, and molecular-sieve techniques are shown not only to form the basis of serum protein separations but also to result in operational classifications. It is revealed also in Chapter 3, where the class of immunoglobulins is operationally defined.

The definitive classification of the ASBC-APS system of 1907 prematurely announced what apparently was regarded as near final compilation of protein knowledge. Hindering more than helping scientific advancement, it attempted to establish, in fact, a theoretical basis for a subject that was clearly still very much analytical and that only now is beginning to reach the fringes of the third stage of scientific development.

Modern protein chemistry, with its foundations secure in concepts of molecular biology, is beginning to adapt itself to a fact of nature that it had previously attempted to avoid—the fact of individuality among molecules created by *biological variescence*. Giving rise to heterogeneity within a particular functional protein species, variescence (a term invented by C. S. Peirce, 1911, to mean a change that produces an uncompensated increment in the number of independent elements of a situation) merely expresses in a particular molecular way the diversity created by adaptive, genetic, and evolutionary processes in biology. Thus, two molecular members of a particular type of enzyme may be quite similar in their active sites, even congruent, and yet vary extensively in their tertiary structures. The active sites of two antibody molecules from separate individuals may have the same conformation, yet vary in their allotypic structures that are genetically determined.

As modern protein chemistry begins to embrace the concept of heterogeneity (aided not a little by analytical immunochemistry) it also begins to free itself from the operational demands of analytical precision and to base its definitive theory upon the action of functional groups. The investigators of structural and functional aspects of the immunoglobulins, as presented in these pages, have, themselves, played a major rôle in this current transition in protein science. Studies on the heterogeneity of the active sites of antibodies, in particular, reveal that two protein molecules from the same individual population may even be structurally quite similar for the most part and allotypically homogeneous, yet be considerably heterogeneous with respect to functional reactivity.

Crystallinity has long been taught as one of the ultimate criteria of homogeneity and purity of a particular substance. Stemming from the more precise sciences of inorganic chemistry, it long ago moved from an operational method of classification to one more definitive. By the time Sumner (1926) had succeeded in crystallizing a functional protein enzyme—urease—for the first time, science was ready to accept this operational separation as a definitive classification. As more and more individual proteins reached the stage of crystallizability, those that continually defied crystallization were held to be considerably more impure, among them the alkaline phosphatases and the immunoglobulins. Edsall and Wyman (1958) have pointed out, however, that even protein crystals, with their wide range of composition with respect to water and salt content, cannot be assumed to be constant with respect to the chemical potential of the protein component itself. Even more telling is the heterogeneity of crystalline Fraction III of papain-fragmented rabbit immuno-γ-globulin (IgG), which, when solubilized and subjected to zonal electrophoresis, separates into several distinct components (Gitlin and Merler, 1961; Putnam, 1965).

Crystallization, although removed from its lofty definitive position, still remains a most valuable operational technique that provides material that can be explored by X-ray diffraction techniques. Indeed, even in the realm of inorganic chemistry, crystallization is not always eminently definitive. For example, it is now known from diffraction studies that deformities within inorganic crystals must be *created*, if not found that way in nature, in order to make certain of the crystals' *function* as phosphors, and certain others, as semiconductors. Hence, even in as "pure" a science as inorganic chemistry, many functional aspects depend on deviations from Berzelian stoichiometry. Modern transistors would not be possible without such deviations.

Protein chemistry as a science had its real beginnings at a time when the influence of the Swedish chemist, Berzelius (1779–1848), was uppermost. His remarkable contributions to chemical formulations through considerations of stoichiometry were so thoroughly felt during his lifetime that the English medical journal, *The Lancet*, in Volume II, 1847, expressed great concern over his ill health. It was in this same volume that the lectures of Professor H. Bence Jones on chemical pathology, expressing great confidence in the Berzelian method, appeared.

Professor Jones, although he was sure that a single formulation could be obtained for an elemental protein radical, could not decide whether the Dutch chemist, Mulder, or the German chemist, Liebig, was right (Jones, 1847). Mulder had been responsible for conferring the Greek word πρωτειος (*proteios*), meaning primary or foremost, upon a group of animal substances, such as fibrin, albumin, and leucine, but he felt that the primary or protein radical common to all of them was confined to a stoichiometric compound containing carbon, nitrogen, oxygen, and hydrogen, but no sulfur. In cases where extra oxygen or sulfur appeared, these were considered to be derivative of Mulder's protein radical.

Thus Mulder (1838) had written:

> Um die analysirten Körper zu unterscheiden, habe ich die in dem Fibrin u.s.w. enthaltene thierische Materie *Protéin* genannt; Pr + SP ist also Fibrin; Pr + S₂P Albumin von Serum u.s.w.- Die Verbindung mit Schwefelsäure könnte *Proteinschwefelsäure* (acide sulpho-protéïque), die gelbe Säure *Xanthoproteinsäure* genannt werden. Zur Unterscheidung der extractartigen Materien habe ich das farblose Extract *Protid*, das rothe Extract *Erythroprotid* genannt.

By 1846 a bitter controversy had developed between Mulder and Liebig over the question of whether the primary protein radical should or should not contain sulfur, and finally one of Liebig's students, after a lengthy analytical presentation (Laskowski, 1846), concluded:

> ... dass, da die Annahme des von Hrn. Mulder unter dem namen Proteïn beschriebenen Körpers sich bloss darauf gründete, das man denselben schwefelfrei isolirt zu haben glaubte,—der von Hrn. Mulder isolirte Körper aber schwefelhaltig und der von ihm beschriebene nicht isolirbar ist—, selbst kein Grund vorhanden ist. das Proteïn als hypothetischen Grundstoff anzunehmen.

Mulder's theories were dashed, but the name he chose, protein, survived.

Liebig by this time was so enraged by Mulder's opposition to him (Moulton, ed., 1942) that he furiously applied himself to protein analyses, and in the same year (Liebig, 1846) obtained a new crystalline compound, resulting from the fusion of potassium hydroxide with casein, as well as leucine. In a noteworthy paper extending his findings to fibrin and serum albumin, Liebig (1847) obtained the same compound, presented a correct analysis of it (which was hastily and incorrectly given in the 1846 paper), and named it tyrosine from the Greek τυρός, meaning cheese. He also found, analyzed, and named sarcosine (σάρς, σαρχός, meaning flesh) and inosinic acid (ἴς, ἴνος, meaning muscle). By 1849 another of Liebig's students (Bopp, 1849) had turned to acid hydrolysis as a far better technique than KOH fusion and had easily obtained crystalline tyrosine from albumin, casein, and fibrin, thus confirming Liebig's own work.

The structural aspects of protein chemistry were firmly established by this work and amino acid analysis became the means of operational classification. For the next 110 years definitive protein stoichiometry was forcefully sought but never really obtained. Scientists blamed themselves and their faulty techniques for never having reached the pinnacle of homogeneity, and looked to the amino acid analyzer to do what they had failed to accomplish. The analyzer merely taught in a more definitive way what manual assays had already indicated—the lesson of biological variescence. Thus, it is only now, as protein chemistry begins to divest itself from the confining bonds of Liebig's stoichiometry, that Mulder's word, protein, takes on the true significance of a primary functional element of living matter. Heterogeneity, biological variescence, molecular individuality—these are the essence of the primary stuff of life.

REFERENCES

Bopp, F. (1849). Einiges über Albumin, Caseïn und Fibrin. J. Liebig's Ann. Chem. *69:* 16–37.

Edsall, J. T., and Wyman, J. (1958). *Biophysical Chemistry*, Vol. I, Academic Press (New York, 699 pp.), p. 320.

Gitlin, D., and Merler, E. (1961). A comparison of the peptides released from related rabbit antibodies by enzymatic hydrolysis. J. Exptl. Med. *114:* 217–230.

Jones, H. Bence (1847). Papers on chemical pathology, Lecture III. Lancet *2:* 88–92.

Kendall, F. E. (1937). Studies on serum proteins. I. Identification of a single serum globulin by immunological means. Its distribution in the sera of normal individuals and of patients with cirrhosis of the liver and with chronic glomerulonephritis. J. Clin. Invest. *16:* 921–931.

Laskowski, N. (1846). Ueber die Proteïntheorie. J. Liebig's Ann. Chem. *58:* 129–166.

Liebig, J. (1846). Baldriansäure und ein neuer Körper aus Käsestoff. J. Liebig's Ann. Chem. *57:* 127–129.

Liebig, J. (1847). Ueber die Bestundtheile der Flussigkeiten des Fleisches. J. Liebig's Ann. Chem. *62:* 257–369.

Moulton, F. R., ed. (1942). *Liebig and After Liebig. A Century of Progress in Agricultural Chemistry.* Symposium. AAAS Publication No. 16, Washington, D. C.

Mulder, G. W. (1838). Zusammensetzung von Fibrin, Albumin, Leimzucker, Leucin, u.s.w. J. Liebig's Ann. Chem. *28:* 73–82.

Peirce, C. S. (1911). Letter to Lady Welby, May 22, 1911. In *Values in a Universe of Chance, Selected Writings of Charles S. Peirce*, Wiener, P. P., ed., Doubleday Anchor Books (Garden City, N. Y., 446 pp., 1958), pp. 428–430.

Putnam, F. W. (1965). Structure and function of the plasma proteins. In *The Proteins*, 2nd Ed., Vol. III, Neurath, H., ed., Academic Press (New York, pp. 153–267), p. 241.

Schultze, H. E. (1962). Influence of bound sialic acid on electrophoretic mobility of human serum proteins. Arch. Biochem. Biophys. Suppl. 1, 290–294.

Sumner, J. B. (1926). The isolation and crystallization of the enzyme urease. Preliminary paper. J. Biol. Chem. *69:* 435–441.

2

The Physical Chemistry of Serum

Tiselius (1937b) first described the constituents of serum in terms of their electrophoretic mobility. He named the separated fractions in the globulin group as α, β, and γ, in accordance with the order in which they followed albumin as moving waves of protein. Depending upon pH, ionic strength, and temperature, mobilities of the components could be changed, but under acceptable standard conditions they were exceedingly reproducible. Since the rate of migration of a given component is proportional to the potential gradient applied, the ratio between the two is a constant, characteristic of that component. The constant is called mobility (μ) and is measured generally in terms of

$$\mu = \frac{\text{rate of migration}}{\text{potential gradient}} = \left[\frac{\text{cm/sec}}{\text{volt/cm}}\right] = [\text{cm}^2 \text{ volt}^{-1} \text{ sec}^{-1}]$$

Since actual mobility values of serum proteins in these terms are of the order of 10^{-5}, it is the usual practice to employ a factor of 10^5 to bring the values within the range of units. A sign, plus or minus, is also used to indicate whether the protein moves toward the cathode or the anode. At a pH of 8.6 all the serum proteins are on the alkaline side of their isoelectric points, all are negatively charged, and all move toward the positive terminal or anode. Their mobilities under such conditions carry a negative sign. At the isoelectric point pI where a given protein is neutral, no movement occurs and the mobility is zero.

Electrophoretic mobility curves for purified human serum proteins and for bovine serum albumin as a function of pH (Fig. 1) indicate the shift in electrophoretic patterns that occurs as one changes the pH of the system. Putnam (1965a) refers to "our mental picture of the plasma protein system" as one that often overlooks the fact that it is based upon resolution at the standard Veronal buffer with a pH of 8.6. Indeed, it would be more helpful in our thinking if our mental picture were to be focused more upon the mobility curves than upon the single pH patterns. However, even with this more general picture in mind, it must be remembered that both mobilities and isoelectric points depend somewhat upon ionic strength and upon the nature of the buffer salts employed.

Since the transport of a mixture of proteins from a starting point through an electric field results in time in a separation of the mixture by virtue of differences in charge, a banding effect results in the electrophoretic cell in terms of protein concentration. The bands of colorless proteins can be observed by absorption of ultraviolet light (280

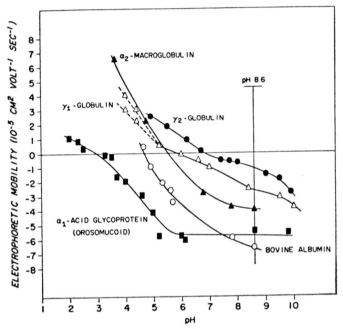

Fig. 1. Electrophoretic mobility curves of purified human serum proteins and of bovine serum albumin. (Putnam, 1965a.)

mμ), by changes in refractive index, by interferometry, or by other optical means, and through special optical systems can be seen to move as boundaries during an electrophoretic run according to their respective mobilities. Photographs taken at any given time through such optical systems provide an instant plot of protein concentration against distance from the starting point. Integration of the curves obtained from enlargements of these photographs gives an expression of the protein content in each band. An example of a plasma electrophoretogram used for estimation of concentrations of components is illustrated in Figure 2. Although in practice there is much more to the technique of

Fig. 2. Moving-boundary electrophoresis of normal serum (*top*) and hyper-gammaglobulinemic serum (*bottom*). Descending limb. (Korngold, 1961).

free-boundary electrophoresis than that just given (cf. Tiselius, 1930, 1937a), in principle and for our purposes the description should suffice. What one should keep in mind is that such electrophoretic runs do not separate a mixture of proteins of similar charge density nor do they separate compounds of dissimilar mobility that have a strong affinity for each other. In fact, use is made of the strong binding affinity of albumin for dyes of much greater mobility in visual tracing of albumin boundaries. The dyes, when absorbed to albumin in small amounts so as not to change albumin mobility perceptibly, move with the protein in electrophoresis. It is often the case that reproducible homogeneity of a band of protein obtained at a given pH and ionic strength may display further separation under other conditions.

Another means of effecting subdivision of protein bands that appear homogeneous in the free-flow moving-boundary process is by employ-ment of what Tiselius termed zone electrophoresis. In this case charged proteins are forced to flow through a solvent that is confined to a micro-porous supporting medium such as filter paper, starch, various types of gels, or cellulose acetate. The distance traveled by the charged group is therefore lengthy because of the winding solvent channels it must tra-verse, and its resolution is correspondingly better. Surface adsorption and frictional effects also take place on the supporting medium (varying in effectiveness, of course, with the type of support chosen) and provide a chromatographic effect that also tends to separate the various pro-teins still further. In the case of disc electrophoresis through poly-acrylamide gel (Ornstein and Davis, 1962) as many as 20 separate bands can be obtained from fresh human serum in less than an hour in in a total length of less than 5 cm. The gel is so ultramicroporous that it creates discontinuous bands of buffer salts of varying pH and concen-tration when current is applied, and thereby effects the thin banding of proteins exemplified in Figure 3. Identity of the separate components, however, in this extreme example of zone electrophoresis cannot be made according to our mental picture of classical electrophoretograms. Not only are the protein bands multitudinous, but also their order of appearance is not necessarily the same as the order of their mobilities. Either a second dimension must be added such as that used in immu-noelectrophoresis or the separated components must be isolated and identified by some other means.

The immunoelectrophoretic technique of Grabar and Williams (1955) involves first the zonal electrophoresis of serum proteins in agar gel and then diffusion outwards after cessation of electrophoretic movement. Identity of separated components is accomplished by simultaneous diffusion inwards, from a starting line parallel to the developed elec-trophoretogram, of antisera specific for one or several of the serum components. Precipitation arcs become visible between the two lines where antibodies and their respective serum antigens meet, react, and aggregate. Since the diffusion rates of many of the various serum compo-nents vary with size and shape, separation of proteins from electro-phoretically homogeneous zones is accomplished, diffusion is stopped wherever precipitation by antibodies occurs, and identity is made according to the two-dimensional position of the precipitation arcs.

Electrophoresis in agar gel in an appropriate buffer solution does not alter the mobilities of the various serum proteins from those observed in free moving-boundary electrophoresis; however, an endosmotic effect does occur which creates a flow of the liquid phase in the cathodic direc-

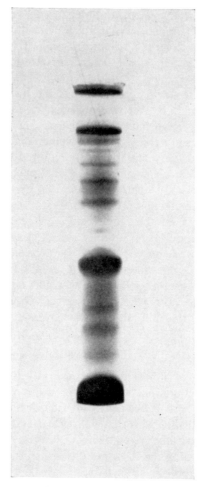

Fig. 3. Disc electrophoresis of human serum in a 0.5 × 4.0 cm column of polyacrylamide gel. Protein was stained with Amido Black 10B. (Ornstein and Davis, 1962.)

tion, counter to the anodic movement of the proteins. This, in effect, translates the final position of the protein bands backwards. Using dye-treated albumin as a marker, one can show that the relative positions of the other proteins are little different from those expected by calculation from mobility constants obtained from free moving-boundary analyses. Having established this fact, Williams and Grabar (1955) were able to assign mobility values to the various components of human serum that were separated by immunoelectrophoresis. Photographs of the precipitin arcs obtained by immunoelectrophoresis are shown in Figure

4 along with the moving-boundary electrophoretic tracing for comparison. Mobilities of the various constituents and the number of components observed in each mobility zone appear in Table 1.

Immunoelectrophoresis is actually an applied variation of the double-diffusion technique of Ouchterlony (1953). Although more will be said later about the immunochemistry basic both to immunoelectrophoresis and double-diffusion techniques, at this juncture the concept of diffusion as a general physical measure of serum proteins will be emphasized. Diffusion of a substance in dilute solution depends upon the frictional forces it must overcome in order to move at a steady rate; the diffusion coefficient D of a substance is inversely related to the frictional force f by the equation

$$D = RT/f$$

where R and T are the gas constant and absolute temperature, respectively, and where f is the amount of force needed to move one mole one centimeter in one second. Since the frictional force depends, in effect, upon the radius r of the molecule upon which it acts, as given by the well-known Stokes law,

$$f = \text{constant}_1 \times r$$

(where the constant is the product of the Avogadro number N and the viscosity η, in the form $6\pi\eta N$), and since the radius is related to molecular weight M by

$$r = \text{constant}_2 \times M^{1/3}$$

[where the constant is the cube root of the quotient of the partial specific volume $\bar{v}$ and N in the form $(3\bar{v}/4\pi N)^{1/3}$], then the frictional coefficient f is also a function of the cube root of the molecular weight,

$$f = \text{constant}_1 \times \text{constant}_2 \times M^{1/3}$$

and the diffusion coefficient D bears a relation to molecular weight by

$$\frac{1}{D} = \text{constant}_3 \times M^{1/3}$$

(where the constant$_3$ is constant$_1$ × constant$_2/RT$).

The relationships equated here apply only to relatively large spherical substances. Since many serum protein molecules do not exhibit spherical properties but more often exhibit those characteristic of ellipsoids, two types of frictional forces must be dealt with on the average: those acting proportional to the minor axis of revolution and those proportional to the major axis. Since the surface area of an ellipsoid is greater than that for a sphere of the same volume, the frictional force is also greater. Thus, one can obtain a measure of the elongation or dissymmetry of a protein molecule from the frictional ratio f/f_0 where f is calculated from

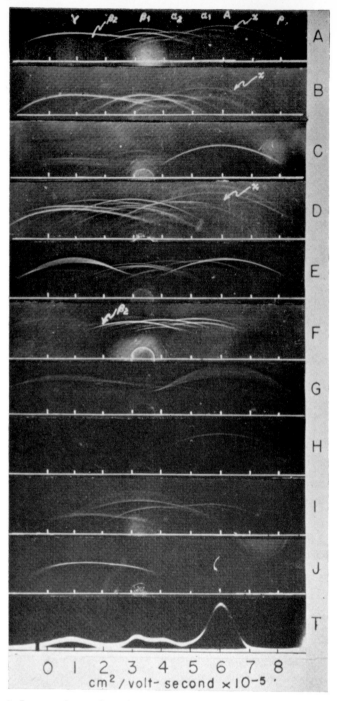

Fig. 4. Immunoelectrophoretic patterns compared with moving-boundary electrophoresis. *A*, basic pattern for total human serum; *B*, antigen excess pattern; *C*, antibody excess pattern; *D*, lyophilized serum in antigen excess; *E*, pateological serum from myeloma patient; *F*, basic pattern with antiserum absorbhd with Cohn fractions II and V; *G*, human serum developed with rabbit antiserum; *H*, Cohn fraction V; *I*, Cohn fraction IV-7; *J*, Cohn fraction γ_1; *T*, schlieren diagram of moving-boundary electrophoresis. (Williams and Grabar, 1955.)

TABLE 1

Immunoelectrophoretic Studies on Human Serum Proteins

Fraction	Mobility*		Number of Components
	Moving boundary	Immunoelectrophoresis	
ρ		7.2–7.8	1
Albumin	5.9–6.1	6.0†	2
α_1	5.3	5.2–5.3,	2
		5.3–5.5	
α_2	4.0–4.2	4.0–4.5	5
β_1	3.0–3.2	3.0–3.2	4
β_2		2.1–2.4	1
γ_1	1.7	1.4–1.6	Family
		†	
γ	0.7–0.9	0.7–1.0	Family

(From Williams and Grabar, 1955.)

* At pH 8.2; $\mu = 0.1$; 3.92 v/cm applied.

† Fixes relative position; by accepting these values from moving boundary, other values could be determined.

actual diffusion data and f_0 is calculated on the basis of spherical molecules.

Although precise diffusion data can be obtained only by rigorous measurements of the free diffusion of purified substances in specially designed analytical diffusion cells, semiquantitative data can be obtained in agar-gel systems. We have already seen in the immunoelectrophoresis photographs of human serum the qualitative differentiation of high and low molecular weight substances of the same electrophoretic mobility on the basis of slow and fast diffusion. To illustrate a semiquantitative application, the determination of D for bovine conglutinin (Lachmann and Richards, 1964) using the L-plate method of Allison and Humphrey (1960) is shown in Figure 5. Although we have not as yet discussed the antigen-antibody precipitation reaction, it is obvious that in order to calculate diffusion data for antigen the diffusion coefficient of antibody must be known. The two starting lines *OG* and *OB* for diffusion of antigen and antibody form a right angle and the precipitation line *P* forms between them. The angle *GOP* represents diffusion of antigen; *BOP*, of antibody.

$$\tan (\angle\ GOP) = (D_G/D_B)^{1/2}$$

where D_G and D_B are the diffusion coefficients of antigen and antibody, respectively.

Rates of sedimentation of proteins in an ultracentrifugal field vary partially and directly with molecular weight and, under appropriate standard conditions of concentration (partial specific volume), density,

Fɪɢ. 5. L-plate method for measuring diffusion of bovine conglutinin. The angle between the antigen trough and the precipitation line is 25°. (Lachmann and Richards, 1964.)

viscosity, and temperature, can be measured directly. In an analytical ultracentrifuge, as in free moving-boundary electrophoresis, special optical systems, through which moving boundaries of sedimenting proteins can be observed, aid in the detection of components separating from a mixture. However, rates of sedimentation (v/unit field) depend not only upon molecular weights but also upon rates of diffusion by the relation

$$v/\text{unit field} = \text{constant}_4 \times D \times M$$

[where $\text{constant}_4 = (1 - \bar{v}\rho)/RT$, and v/unit field = velocity of sedimentation per unit gravitational field].

It is more common to express the velocity of sedimentation through a unit gravitational field in terms of s_{20}^0, designated as Svedberg units of 10^{-13} sec. A unit field is given in terms of dynes/gram or cm/sec^2; velocity, in cm/sec; and velocity/unit field, in seconds. Under standard conditions, the term S stands fortuitously for Svedberg units, seconds, and sedimentation time.

Diffusion runs counter to sedimentation since it measures the tendency of a solute to pass from higher to lower concentration (unit concentration gradient) across a unit cross-sectional area in a given time (usually with units of cm^2/sec). Thus, for a given molecular weight the ratio of sedimentation and diffusion will be constant but the individual diffusion and sedimentation coefficients may vary with each other and go up or down. Just as the frictional force f interferes with diffusion it also opposes sedimentation such that

$$f = \frac{RT}{D} = \frac{M(1 - \bar{v}\rho)}{s}$$

When a three-dimensional graph is constructed relating the relative distributions of serum components to the electrophoretic mobilities and sedimentation rates of those components, a diagram such as that of Figure 6 is obtained. Yet another construct could be made substituting diffusion coefficients for sedimentation rates. It is again clear as with immunoelectrophoresis that applying a second dimension to initial electrophoretic separation provides a widened and more detailed picture of the complex multicomponent serum system.

Another method that effects partial separation of serum components according to molecular size involves the use of molecular sieves. Cross-linked dextran gels (Sephadex, AB, Pharmacia, Uppsala, Sweden) can be made that exclude molecules above a certain size but which freely allow smaller sized molecular species to pass into the interior of the gel matrix (Porath and Flodin, 1959). Since the internal aqueous volume of the gels is very high compared with the external volume, fairly effective separations of large and small molecules can be accomplished. A column of Sephadex G-200, for example, completely excludes the high molecular weight α- and β-lipoproteins and the 19S α_2- and β_2-macroglobulins, partially excludes the 7S γ-globulins, and permits free internal passage of 4.6S serum albumin. As shown in Figure 7, the high molecular weight proteins appear in the column effluent first, the 7S γ-globulin next, and albumin last. Identification of separated components according to order of appearance in the effluent is not, however, a safe way of designating relative molecular sizes without subsequent ultracentrifugal analysis of the individual protein components.

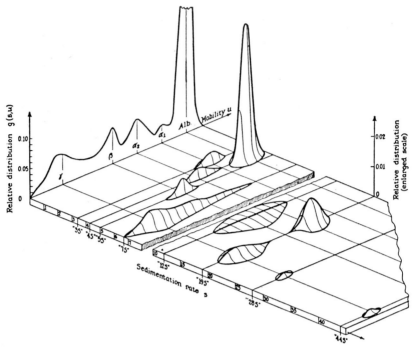

Fig. 6. Three-dimensional diagram showing the electrophoretic and ultracentrifugal components of normal lipid-free serum. Scale is enlarged in the *right-hand* part. *1*, albumin; *2*, prealbumin; *3*, 3.5S α₁-glycoproteins; *4*, haptoglobin; *5*, hemopexin; *6*, transferrin; *7*, 7S γ-globulin; *8*, ceruloplasmin; *9*, IgA; *10*, α₂-mucoprotein; *11*, α₂-macroglobulin; *12*, IgM. (Wallenius, Trautman, Kunkel, and Franklin, 1957.) See Chapter 3 for explanation of IgA and IgM.

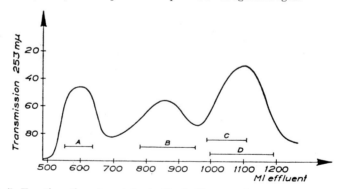

Fig. 7. Fractionation of proteins in 50 ml of human plasma on Sephadex G-200. Eluent, 0.1 M Tris + 1 M NaCl, pH 8.0; elution rate, 68 ml/hour; column size, 7 × 50 cm. Region *A*, IgM, α₂M globulins, α- and β-lipoproteins, and fibrinogen; *B*, IgG and other 7S immunoglobulins; *C*, transferrin; *D*, albumin. (Flodin, 1962, as reported by Porath, 1962.) See Chapter 3 for explanation of IgM and α₂M.

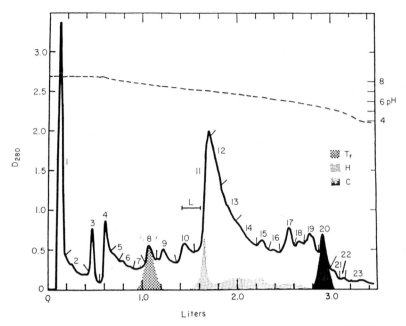

Fɪɢ. 8. Effluent diagram of human serum chromatographed on DEAE-cellulose. Tris-phosphate gradient buffer from 0.005 м to 0.5 м. *Solid line*, absorption
at 280 mμ; dashed line, pH. *L*, lipoprotein; T_f, transferrin; *H*, haptoglobin-heme
(absorption at 405 mμ); *C*, ceruloplasmin. (Sober and Peterson, 1958.)

Chromatographic columns in which ion-exchange systems are incorporated into the solid adsorbent phase provide a method for separating mixtures according to charge. Peterson and Sober (1956) prepared
diethylaminoethyl-cellulose columns (DEAE-cellulose) that, by virtue
of their weakly anionic-exchange properties, could be used to separate
serum proteins according to charge. The profiles (Figure 8) (Sober and
Peterson, 1958) were dissimilar to electrophoretic mobility profiles since
the charge density of a particular protein was not the sole criterion for
adsorption to the ion-exchange column. For a large protein of low charge
density the number of bands established with the ion exchanger could
still be numerous, and the total molecular binding strength could be
greater in some cases than that for a low molecular weight substance
with a high charge density. Thus, the 19S IgM, a macro-γ-globulin
with a low mobility, was found by Fahey and Horbett (1959) to exhibit
tighter binding than highly mobile albumin.

As in electrophoresis, however, pH and ionic strength are particularly
important in ion-exchange chromatography. Unlike electrophoresis, on
the other hand, where standard conditions fix pH and ionic strength at

established levels, ion-exchange chromatography frequently and most effectively takes place under constantly (gradient) or stepwise changing pH and/or ionic strength. The actual conditions chosen depend on what particular component of serum more than any other is desired in the greatest purity. For example, to subfractionate the immunoglobulin complex into four groups of 6.6S components and one of 18S, Fahey and Horbett (1959) adsorbed the complex at pH 8 and 0.02 M Tris-phosphate, and eluted with a developing solvent that was constantly increasing in ionic strength to 0.3 M (Fig. 9).

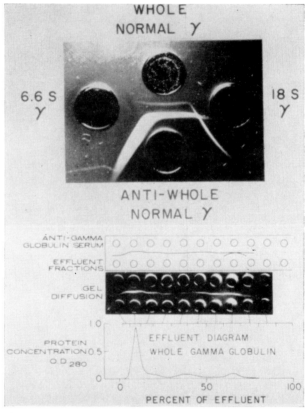

FIG. 9. Characterization of chromatographic fractions of human immunoglobulins obtained from DEAE-cellulose columns (*lower section*). Rabbit antiserum was used as reagent. In the *upper section* is a gel-diffusion characterization of IgM in a case of macroglobulinemia, showing its immunochemical identity with a normal immunoglobulin. (Fahey and Horbett, 1959.) See Chapter 3 for explanation of IgM.

The electrophoretic mobility curves as a function of pH (Fig. 1) showed that γ-globulin has an isoelectric point of about 7.3. Below this pH the protein is positively charged, cathode seeking, and, of course, unreactive with anion exchangers. At lower pH's, therefore, where some other serum components would still be negatively charged, γ-globulin would separate by virtue of non-reactivity. To subfractionate the positively charged material, cation exchangers can be used. Thus cation-exchange columns, exemplified by carboxymethyl-cellulose (CM-cellulose), at a weakly acid pH, have provided another medium for subfractionation of immunoglobulins. Sober and Peterson (1958) adsorbed their protein mixture of hyperimmune globulin on CM-cellulose at pH 6.6 and 0.015 M sodium phosphate, eluted by a gradient which increased both in pH and in ionic strength to pH 7.65 and 0.1 M sodium chloride-0.2 M sodium phosphate. Immunochemically active subcomponents were obtained with distinctive electrophoretic mobilities.

A century-old but still extremely valuable empirical method for partially resolving a protein mixture and separating a given component from several others is known as "salting-out." A fairly rigorous theoretical treatment of this phenomenon is given by Edsall and Wyman (1958), the essence of which is still largely empirical with respect to salting-out of proteins. At high ionic strengths of salts such as ammonium sulfate, sodium sulfate, and the various phosphate buffer systems, relatively small increments in salt concentration result in protein precipitation such that the logarithm of protein solubility S_p decreases proportionally with increasing salt concentration (given in terms of ionic strength or $\Gamma/2$),

$$\log (S_p) = \log (S_i) - K_s(\Gamma/2).$$

The term $\log S_i$ is the extrapolated value of the relation back to zero ionic strength, an ideal hypothetical solubility in a salt-free system. The term K_s is the slope of the line obtained by plotting $\log S_p$ against $\Gamma/2$ and is called the salting-out constant. The plots shown in Figure 10 for a variety of proteins indicate the precision of the relation. With changes in pH and temperature the lines generally become translated upwards or downwards, thus changing $\log S_i$ but not K_s. Edsall and Wyman (1958) point out, therefore, that salting-out with increasing ionic strength proceeds independently of electric charge and temperature of the protein solution although its initial effective starting point is very much dependent upon charge and temperature.

Although it is not our purpose to belabor the multitude of recipes available for separations, the prevalence of ammonium and sodium

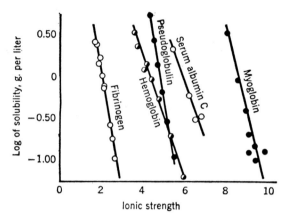

Fig. 10. Salting-out of proteins. (Cohn and Edsall, 1943, as reported by Edsall and Wyman, 1958.)

sulfate procedures for γ-globulin separation, in particular, make mention of these two worthwhile. Ammonium sulfate, because of its greater solubility in cold water, provides a reagent for achieving the desired high ionic strength under better conditions of protein preservation at low temperatures. On the other hand, sodium sulfate, because of its sharper resolution, is often preferred, and, in cases where subsequent nitrogen determinations of separated protein are desired, sodium sulfate is actually required. In the case of ammonium sulfate, saturated solutions are frequently maintained as stock reagents over a solid phase to maintain constant concentration, but it makes a difference at what temperature equilibrium between insoluble and soluble phases is maintained. Commonly, 34 % saturated ammonium sulfate is used for globulin precipitation; i.e., the final concentration is 34 % of the saturated concentration. For those who hesitate to dump solid ammonium sulfate even of the correct amount into serum and who dislike the uncertainties of saturated solution maintenance, deliberate preparation of 67 % saturated ammonium sulfate by formula is often utilized. One volume each of plasma and reagent achieves the final desired concentration.

Sodium sulfate is generally described in terms of weight-volume percent. A stock reagent of 27 % is kept at 30°C, and 2 volumes added to 1 volume of serum make a final concentration of 18 % which precipitates much of the globulin from solution and leaves albumin in solution. Precipitation at 13.5 % (1 volume each of reagent and plasma) still renders γ-globulin and some β-globulin insoluble whereas α-globulins remain soluble.

In all salt precipitation techniques, although high purity of individual components is rarely achieved, considerable improvement in purity is accomplished by dissolving and re-precipitating the initial insoluble components two or three more times. As can be seen from a consideration of Figure 10, the closer the precipitation lines of two components come, the harder it is to achieve separation. In order to obtain maximum separation in such cases, a sacrifice in yield must be made by precipitating the least soluble component at a lower ionic strength than would result in complete precipitation. By this means the more soluble component may often come within a completely soluble range.

Protein precipitation with aqueous solutions of organic solvents such as methanol and ethanol occurs as a result of a decrease in polarity of the solvent phase. Because of dangers of protein denaturation, temperatures must be maintained as close to freezing as is feasible. The higher the ethanol concentration, the lower the freezing point, of course; thus, subzero temperatures can and must be maintained. In the Cohn fractionation Method 10, the additional use of the zinc cation in low concentrations made it possible to limit the maximum alcohol concentration to 19%. A complete scheme for separating plasma into eight major fractions and into several subfractions was accomplished and automated for industrial application (Pennell, 1960). According to Putnam (1965b), however, "the ethanol method is falling into disuse in the research laboratory since the advent of protein chromatography on cellulose ion-exchange columns." Putnam reveals that the cold ethanol methods continue to be exploited commercially, and that at the time of the Cuban crisis a stockpile of 5,000,000 gm (5.5 tons) of γ-globulin had been created.

Partly because of the success of the specific and reversible combining activity of Zn^{++} with plasma proteins, revived interest in other cationic interactions with proteins as a basis for precipitation has occurred. Of these the observations by Lewin (1954) and by Rejnek and Škvařil (1957) on the action of Al^{+++} are of greatest interest in this context. γ-Globulin alone fails to form insoluble complexes with the aluminum cation and can be obtained directly in 95% purity and 80–90% yield.

Similar to the action of Al^{+++}, the acridine dye, Rivanol [2-ethoxy-6,9-diaminoacridine (lactate)], causes precipitation of all plasma proteins with the exception of γ-globulin (Hořejši and Smetana, 1956). The latter can be recovered in 97–98% purity. Polyphosphates can also be used to precipitate all but γ-globulin to produce a product of greater than 90% purity (Nitschmann, Rickli, and Kistler, 1960).

Specific salts for the precipitation of other members of the γ-globulin family have not as yet been thoroughly investigated although there is certainly a definite need. A step in this direction, however, is the method of Heremans (1960) for the separation of immunoglobulin A (IgA, formerly designated as β_2A or γ_1A). Taking cognizance of Kunkel's zinc sulfate turbidity test, which had been used to classify certain serum proteins according to solubility (Kunkel, 1947), Heremans used "the discriminant action of zinc ions" in separating a fairly pure fraction of IgA (Heremans and Heremans, 1961).

Serum-protein profiles obtained by one or more of the operational techniques so far listed have proven to be of extreme value in the clinic for establishing clinically normal values and for indicating possible disease states by shifts in the profiles. On occasion clinical reports of abnormal serum profiles reveal the appearance of unique new components that are missing from the normal picture. One of these (Waldenström, 1944) reported the appearance of large amounts of a high molecular weight globulin in three patients with incipient myelomatosis. Pedersen established by ultracentrifuge studies (reported by Waldenström) that the abnormal globulins had sedimentation coefficients of 19–20.6S and by electrophoretic analyses that they had mobilities characteristic of β-globulins. It was only later that this component was recognized in normal human serum, designated as β_2-macroglobulin or γ_1-macroglobulin, and now referred to as IgM, an ordinary member of the class of human immunoglobulins.

In another clinical situation Wuhrmann, Wunderly, and Hassig (1950) noticed that human cases of multiple myeloma (malignancies derived from normal plasma cells) were characterized in part by a theretofore unknown and distinct serum globulin as well as by abnormal amounts of recognizable globulins. The new globulin with a sedimentation coefficient of 7S and a β-like mobility was found shortly thereafter, by antigenic analysis, to be another bypassed member of normal serum, and became known as β_2A- or γ_1A-globulin, now referred to as IgA, yet another member of the class of human immunoglobulins.

It was to be expected that within such a rich accumulation of serum globulins produced by neoplastic plasma cells, other globulin species would be found to join the heterogeneous family of immunoglobulins. Thus, Rowe and Fahey (1965) discovered another distinct immunoglobulin group in myeloma protein and immediately found its counterpart in normal serum at a level of about 1 % of the total immunoglobulin normally present. The new globulin was designated IgD to distinguish it from IgA, IgM, and the classical γ_2-globulin, IgG. (The analytical properties of these four members of the immunoglobulin family will be discussed in detail in subsequent chapters.) Final recognition of the presence of IgD in normal serum depended upon having a specific antibody reagent with which IgD would react. Its physico-chemical properties of electrophoretic mobility, sedimentation, and diffusion were not different enough from many other globulins, and its concentration was too low to indicate its presence in the plasma profile by these operational methods. By immunoelectrophoresis, however, and by application of an antibody specifically reactive with myeloma IgD, normal IgD was uncovered.

A lesson to be learned from such studies is two-fold: that the discovery of an apparently unique substance associated with a particular disease state does not necessarily indicate that the substance is, in fact, unique and specific for that disease; and that one's operational view of a normal state is certainly not to be taken as a definitive one.

The over-all serum profiles as measured by physico-chemical methods do not vary to any great extent from one mammalian species to the next although differences either in concentration or in certain of the molecular parameters do exist for particular components (Putnam, 1965c). Greater differences among species occur, however, in chemical composition. The N-terminal amino acid of rabbit serum albumin, for example, is glutamic acid, whereas in the serum albumins of man, horse, and cow it is asparagine. The amino acid second from the N-terminal end in human serum albumin is alanine rather than the threonine of equine and bovine albumins. At the C-terminal end man and rabbit both have leucine, whereas horse and cow have alanine (Putnam, 1965d, for more complete data and for references). The most striking differences of all, indicative of their occurrence in relatively small structural units, are those made manifest by studies of immunological cross-reactivity among the serum proteins of various mammals.

One needs to look further down the scale of vertebrate classification to find omission of major components that characterize the mammalian serum profile. The comparative immunoelectrophoretic analyses by Papermaster, Condie, Finstad, and Good (1964), shown in Figure 11, exemplify the close relationship between human and dogfish sera. In the serum of the lamprey, a much more primitive species, the γ-globulin part of the profile is scanty with only a single band of slow β- or fast γ-mobility. In the serum of one of the most primitive of the true vertebrates, the hagfish, there is no evidence of any γ-globulin. (The relationship of these findings to the evolution of antibody-forming capacity in vertebrates has been discussed by Good and Papermaster, 1964.)

The comprehensive review by Engle and Woods (1960) on the com-

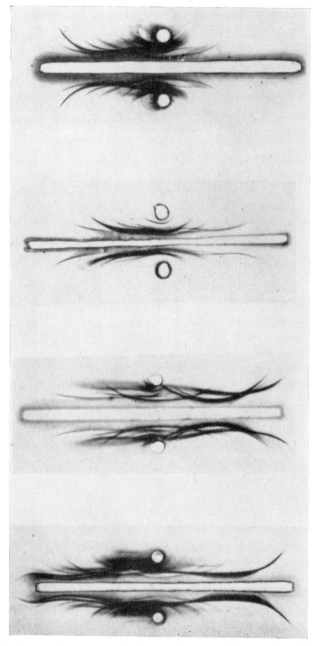

FIG. 11. Immunoelectrophoresis of serum from hagfish (*top*), lamprey, dogfish, and human. (Papermaster, Condie, Finstad, and Good, 1964.)

Frog
  Rana pipiens
Turtle
  Pseudomys floridana mobiliensis
Eastern indigo snake
  Drymarchon corais couperi
Yellow rat snake
  Elaphe obsoleta quadrivittava
Pigeon
  Columba livia
Chicken, white leghorn
  Gallus gallus
Turkey, bronze
  Meleagris gallopavo
Dog
  Canis familiaris
Rat
  Rattus norweigicus
Mouse, A-K strain
  Mus musculus
Rabbit
  Lepus caniculus
Rhesus monkey
  Macaca mulatta
Man
  Homo sapiens

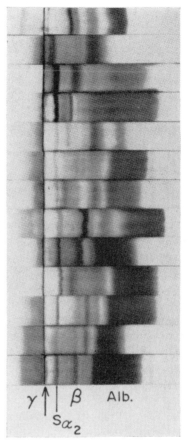

Fig. 12. Starch-gel electrophoresis of serum from amphibia, reptiles, birds and mammals. From *top* to *bottom:* frog, turtle, eastern indigo snake, yellow rat snake, pigeon, white Leghorn chicken, bronze turkey, dog, rat, A-K strain mouse, rabbit, rhesus monkey, man. The cathode is to the *left* of the arrow; the anode, to its *right*. (Woods, Paulsen, Engle, and Pert, 1957; Castillo, Woods, and Engle, 1959, as reported by Engle and Woods, 1960.)

parative biochemistry and embryology of serum proteins is a most rewarding work that presents the serum profiles of a large number of species in terms of their electrophoretic mobilities at pH 8.6 and ionic strength of 0.1. An example is the comparative zonal electrophoretic patterns of some amphibia, reptiles, birds, and mammals that are shown in Figure 12.

The comparative immunoelectrophoretic patterns of primate sera have received particular attention by Williams and Wemyss (1961). By

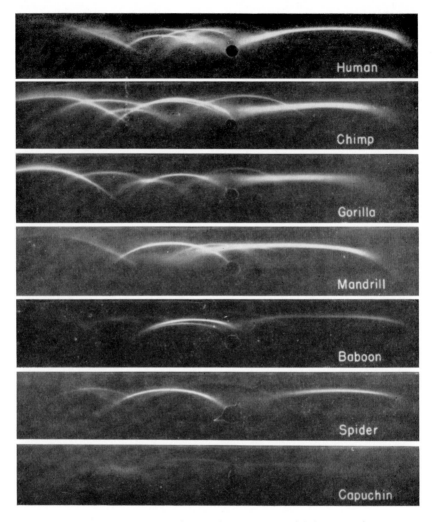

Fig. 13. Immunoelectrophoresis of primate serum with horse antiserum, arranged from *top* to *bottom* according to relationship to man. (Williams and Wemyss, 1961.)

using an antibody reagent against human serum components and arranging the patterns produced with this reagent in decreasing order of presumed primate relationship to man (Figure 13), the authors were able to establish that "generally speaking . . . there are fewer and fewer strong reactions in the patterns as the systematic relationships become more remote." More will be said about these immunological cross-reactivities later on.

Parallel to phylogenic studies of serum profiles are those of the developing fetus and the new-born, again with particular emphasis upon globulins. The situation in the human is complicated by placental transfer of γ-globulin from mother to fetus, but in those species in which a placental barrier exists, such as the cow, the ewe, and the sow, the new-born serum presents an over-all profile not too different from that of the hagfish. Experimental studies of globulin development in the piglet in particular appear to be most fruitful, but discussion of them is outside the scope of this book. One aspect, however, will be discussed in the chapter on antibody fragments, that of a trace quantity of a 5S γ-globulin in the serum of new-born pigs (Franěk and Říha, 1964) that has some structural features in common with a subunit of adult 7S γ-globulin. Keeping in mind that even the serum profile of the hagfish is operational rather than definitive and that the 5S piglet globulin is in such a low concentration that it could easily have escaped detection, one is inclined to wonder about the possible presence in primitive vertebrate sera of small amounts of incompletely formed or primitive γ-globulin that also may have phylogenic significance.

Components of plasma, equilibrated as they are with lymph, cerebro-spinal fluid, and extravascular tissue fluids, make their appearance in these other areas as well. In certain disease states they also appear in ascitic and blister fluids, in urine and fecal matter, and so forth. Claims are frequently made that in these other areas some unique or specific component, not contained in plasma, has been found. In view of our lack of a precise definition of plasma profiles and of our complete ignorance concerning the dynamic equilibrium that would describe the total body distribution of each plasma component, it would be well for us to reserve judgment on such claims.

The emphasis in this chapter has been upon the rich reservoir of serum that constitutes the main source of immunoglobulins and of antibody reagents, and upon the many ways that it can be fractionated to reveal the nature of its components. The intention has been not to provide detailed methods and procedures for actual separations, but rather to provide a rationale upon which such separations are based and to indicate that the full potential of this reservoir has not yet been realized. From an analytical point of view it is always good practice for the analyst to know in some measure the nature of the source of his reagents.

REFERENCES

Allison, A. C., and Humphrey, J. H. (1960). A theoretical and experimental analysis of double diffusion precipitin reactions in agar gel, and its application to characterization of antigens. Immunology *3*: 95–106.

Cohn, E. J., and Edsall, J. T. (1943). *Proteins, Amino Acids, and Peptides.* Reinhold (New York, 686 pp.), p. 602.

Edsall, J. T., and Wyman, J. (1958). *Biophysical Chemistry*, Vol. I, Academic Press (New York, 699 pp.), p. 320.

Engle, R. L., Jr., and Woods, K. R. (1960). Comparative biochemistry and embryology. In *The Plasma Proteins*, Vol. II, Putnam, F. W., ed., Academic Press (New York, 518 pp.) pp. 183–265.

Fahey, J. L., and Horbett, A. P. (1959). Human γ-globulin fractionation on anion exchange cellulose columns. J. Biol. Chem. *234:* 2645–2651.

Franěk, F., and Říha, I. (1964). Purification and structural characterization of 5S γ-globulin in new-born pigs. Immunochemistry *1:* 49–63.

Good, R. A., and Papermaster, B. W. (1964). Ontogeny and phylogeny of adaptive immunity. Advan. Immunol. *4:* 1–115.

Grabar, P., and Williams, C. A., Jr. (1955). Méthode immuno-électrophorétique d'analyse de mélanges de substances antigeniques. Biochim. Biophys. Acta *17:* 67–74.

Heremans, J. F. (1960). Antigenic relations between the globulins of the gamma system. Protides Biol. Fluids *8:* 127–131.

Heremans, J. F., and Heremans, M.-T. (1961). Immunoelectrophoresis. Acta Med. Scand. Suppl. 367, 27–59.

Horějši, J., and Smetana, R. (1956). The isolation of gamma globulin from blood-serum by Rivanol. Acta Med. Scand. *155:* 65–70.

Korngold, L. (1961). Abnormal plasma components and their significance in disease. Ann. N. Y. Acad. Sci. *94:* 110–130.

Kunkel, H. (1947). Estimation of alterations of serum gamma globulin by a turbidimetric technique. Proc. Soc. Exptl. Biol. Med. *66:* 217–224.

Lachmann, P. J., and Richards, C. B. (1964). Some molecular parameters of bovine conglutinin. Immunochemistry *1:* 37–41.

Lewin, J. (1954). Techniques de préparations des gamma-globulines au Centre national de transfusion sanguine; nouvelles méthodes. Therapie *9:* 523–541.

Nitschmann, H., Rickli, E., and Kistler, P. (1960). Fractionation of human plasmas with polyphosphate. Vox Sanguinis *5:* 232–251.

Ornstein, L., and Davis, B. J. (1962). As reported by Sober, H., Hartley, R., Carrol, W., and Peterson, E., in *The Proteins*, 2nd Ed., Vol. III, Neurath, H., ed., Academic Press (New York, 585 pp.), p. 55.

Ouchterlony, O. (1953). Antigen-antibody reactions in gels. IV. Types of reactions in coordinated systems of diffusion. Acta Pathol. Microbiol. Scand. *32:* 231–240.

Papermaster, B. W., Condie, R. M., Finstad, J., and Good, R. A. (1964). Evolution of the immune response. I. The phylogenetic development of adaptive immunologic responsiveness in vertebrates. J. Exptl. Med. *119:* 105–130.

Pennell, R. B. (1960). Fractionation and isolation of purified components by precipitation methods. In *The Plasma Proteins*, Vol. 1, Putnam, F. W., ed., Academic Press (New York, 420 pp.), pp. 9–50.

Peterson, E. A., and Sober, H. A. (1956). Chromatography of proteins. I. Cellulose ion-exchange adsorbents. J. Am. Chem. Soc. *78:* 751–755.

Porath, J. (1962). Cross-linked dextrans as molecular sieves. Advan. Protein Chem. *17:* 209–226.

Porath, J., and Flodin, P. (1959). Gel filtration: a method for desalting and group separation. Nature *183:* 1657–1659.

Putnam, F. W. (1965a). Structure and function of the plasma proteins. In *The Proteins*, 2nd Ed., Vol. III, Neurath, H., ed., Academic Press (New York, pp. 153–267), p. 165.

Putnam, F. W. (1965b). Structure and function of the plasma proteins. In *The Proteins*, 2nd Ed., Vol. III, Neurath, H., ed., Academic Press (New York, p. 153–267), p. 160.

Putnam, F. W. (1965c). Structure and function of the plasma proteins. In *The Proteins*, 2nd Ed., Vol. III, Neurath, H., ed., Academic Press (New York, pp. 153–267), pp. 174–177.

Putnam, F. W. (1965d). Structure and function of the plasma proteins. In *The Proteins*, 2nd Ed., Vol. III, Neurath, H., ed., Academic Press (New York, pp. 153–267), p. 184.

Rejnek, J., and Škvařil, F. (1957). The effect of metals on plasma proteins. II. Combined use of zinc and aluminum ions for the isolation of γ-globulin from the fraction II + III of human plasma. Chem. Listy *51:* 1952–1954.

Rowe, D. S., and Fahey, J. L. (1965). A new class of human immunoglobulins. I. A unique myeloma protein. II. Normal serum IgD. J. Exptl. Med. *121:* 171–199.

Sober, H. A., and Peterson, E. A. (1958). Protein chromatography on ion exchange cellulose. Federation Proc. *17:* 1116–1126.

Tiselius, A. (1930). The moving boundary method of studying the electrophoresis of proteins. Inaugural Dissertation. Nova Acta Reg. Soc. Sci. Upsaliensis IV *7*, No. 4.

Tiselius, A. (1937a). A new apparatus for electrophoretic analysis of colloidal mixtures. Trans. Faraday Soc. *33:* 524–531.

Tiselius, A. (1937b). Electrophoresis of serum globulin. II. Electrophoretic analysis of normal and immune sera. Biochem. J. *31:* 1464–1477.

Waldenström, J. (1944). Incipient myelomatosis or "essential" hyperglobulinemia with fibrinogenopenia—a new syndrome? Acta Med. Scand. *117:* 216–247.

Wallenius, G., Trautman, R., Kunkel, H. G., and Franklin, E. C. (1957). Ultracentrifugal studies of major non-lipide electrophoretic components of normal human serum. J. Biol. Chem. *225:* 253–267.

Williams, C. A., Jr., and Grabar, P., (1955). Immunoelectrophoretic studies on serum proteins. I. The antigens of human serum. J. Immunol. *74:* 158–168.

Williams, C. A., Jr., and Wemyss, C. T. (1961). Experimental and evolutionary significance of similarities among serum protein antigens of man and the lower primates. Ann. N. Y. Acad. Sci. *94:* 77–92.

Wuhrmann, F. H., Wunderly, C., and Hassig, A. (1950). Immunological investigations in ten cases of plasmacytoma. Brit. J. Exptl. Pathol. *31:* 507–514.

3

Immunoglobulins

1. Definition

Unlike the ASBC-APS committee of 1907, which had been too decisive and premature in its rigid nomenclature of protein classes, the signatories[1] of the 1964 World Health Organization meeting in Prague on the nomenclature of human immunoglobulins provided both a useful system and one open to addition or amendment (WHO, 1964). The WHO committee's definition of immunoglobulins follows:

> Immunoglobulins are proteins of animal origin endowed with known antibody activity, and certain proteins related to them by chemical structure and hence antigenic specificity. Related proteins for which antibody activity has not been demonstrated are included—for example, myeloma proteins, Bence-Jones proteins and naturally occurring sub-units of the immunoglobulins.
>
> Immunoglobulins are not restricted to the plasma but may be found in other body fluids or tissues, such as urine, spinal fluid, lymph-nodes, spleen, etc. Proteins may occur which fulfill the above requirements but which have widely differing physico-chemical properties such as electrophoretic mobility, sedimentation coefficient, and diffusion coefficient, and different chemical properties such as carbohydrate content, amino-acid composition of polypeptide chains, etc. Immunoglobulins do not include the components of the complement system.

It can be seen that only three criteria need be filled to fit a compound into the immunoglobulin class: that it be a protein, that it come from an animal source, and that it have some structural features in common with the other members. It need not necessarily have a biological function, but, when it does, that function is antibody activity.

Historically, much was known about antibody activities before very much was known about antibody structures. Our purpose in this book, however, is not to learn about the structure of antibody through its activity but to learn about its activity after considerations of its structure. Some knowledge of immunological specificity and reactivity must

---

[1] Ceppellini, Dray, Edelman, Fahey, Franěk, Franklin, Goodman, Grabar, Gurvich, Heremans, Isliker, Karush, Press, and Trnka.

be presupposed even when presenting structure before function since the primary methods for classifying the structures are themselves immunological. (Since immunoglobulins from one species can invoke anti-immunoglobulin responses in another, and *vice versa*, they can be considered as antigens as well as carriers of antibody activities.) However, perfectly arbitrary assays of immunoglobulin antigenicity through the use of antibody reagents can be assumed now and explained later on.

2. Nomenclature

It must be emphasized that although the WHO signatories defined immunoglobulins in general terms to cover all animal sources, they provided nomenclature solely for the human immunoglobulins. They did recommend that the same principles be used for other species but did not specify at the time how the species of origin should be designated in abbreviated form.[2] The structures of human immunoglobulins will therefore be presented first in terms of the new notation, and then the structures of immunoglobulins of the rabbit, mouse, horse, guinea pig, and other species will be discussed in terms of variation from those of the human.

IgG or γG

This major class was referred to in the older literature as γ-, 7Sγ-, 6.6Sγ-, γ_2-, or γ_{ss}-globulin. It is composed of two major groups of polypeptide chains, one light and one heavy. The light chains may either be κ or λ, and the heavy chains, γ. The distinguishing structures that are specific for IgG are contained in the heavy or γ-chain. The light chains are common for the most part to all known immunoglobulins but each type of light chain is distinguishable from the other. Thus IgG with κ-chains is designated as IgGK (Type I in the older literature), and IgG with λ-chains is designated IgGL (Type II in the older literature). The structural formula of IgGK is given as $\kappa\gamma\gamma\kappa$, indicating that the light chains are separate and terminal and the heavy chains form a dimer. IgGL is likewise $\lambda\gamma\gamma\lambda$.

IgA or γA

Referred to in earlier literature as β_2A- or γ_1A-globulin, this major group is distinguished by α-heavy chains. The light chains are held in common with IgG. Therefore, two structural formulas can be written: $\kappa\alpha\alpha\kappa$ and $\lambda\alpha\alpha\lambda$ for IgAK and IgAL, respectively.

---

[2] The WHO Reference Centre for Immunoglobulins at the Institute of Biochemistry, Lausanne, Switzerland, will continue registry of notations of new immunoglobulins.

IgD or γD

Not known at the time the nomenclature was established, this new human immunoglobulin, discovered by Rowe and Fahey (1965), is unique in its heavy chains, which are designated δ, but possesses the common type of light chains. Structural formulas are, therefore, κδδκ and λδδλ, indicating IgDK and IgDL, respectively.

IgM or γM

The class of macro-immunoglobulins with a molecular weight of the order of 10^6 contains yet another unique set of heavy chains designated μ. It is the nature of the heavy chain rather than the molecular weight which is emphasized even though μ is an abbreviation for macro. Structural formulas for macroglobulin, indicating the order of chain arrangement, are yet to be worked out. Stoichiometric formulas are given, however, as

$$(\mu_2\kappa_2)_n \text{ and } (\mu_2\lambda_2)_n$$

to indicate the relative proportions of light and heavy chains. For the usual 19S macroglobulins, $n = 5$ or 6, and mercaptoethanol treatment of this pentamer or hexamer results in the four-chain units descriptive of the other immunoglobulins. Regardless of molecular weight this class is written as IgMK or IgML.

3. Analysis

The amino acid composition of typical light and heavy chains reveals some of the possible structural differences that can occur. Data for IgG and IgM are shown in Table 2 and are based upon the acceptance of 20,000 for the molecular weight of light chains and 50,000 for heavy. Slight variations in chain molecular weights can, of course, be expected from one individual immunoglobulin to the next within a class, but would reflect only second-order changes in the compositions given in the table.

It can be seen that major differences between IgG and IgM occur only in the heavy chains and that general uniformity exists in the light (with no attempt to differentiate between κ- and λ-chains).

Another distinguishing feature of each class of immunoglobulins is its carbohydrate content, for which analysis is given in Table 3. The carbohydrates appear to be associated mainly with heavy chains. The small amounts of hexose and hexoamine listed for light chains in Table 2 are thought to reflect contamination but this is not as yet known for sure. Again, the analyses in Table 3 are only representative and, because of globulin heterogeneity within a class, would be expected to vary

TABLE 2

Amino Acid Composition of Human Immunoglobulin Chains

Amino Acid	Light Chains		Heavy Chains	
	IgG	IgM	IgG	IgM
	residues/20,000 gm		*residues/50,000 gm*	
Lysine	10	10	29	20
Histidine	3	2	10	7
Arginine	6	5	12	18
Aspartic acid	13	13	33	34
Threonine	15	15	34	38
Serine	24	24	50	42
Glutamic acid	20	19	39	40
Proline	11	11	33	29
Glycine	11	12	28	28
Alanine	12	12	19	26
Valine	13	13	41	36
Methionine	0.6	0.7	4	5
Isoleucine	5	5	8	13
Leucine	13	13	31	30
Tyrosine	8	8	17	12
Phenylalanine	6	5	13	16
Half-cystine	3	3	7	7
S-Carboxymethylcysteine	1	1	4	3(4?)
Tryptophan	2	3	8	7
Hexose	0.025	0	4	20
Hexosamine	0.2	0.3	4.5	12

(From Cohen and Porter (1964), Tables III and IV. See reference for additional data.)

TABLE 3

Carbohydrate in Human Immunoglobulins

Carbohydrate	IgG	IgA	IgM
	%	%	%
Hexose	1.2	4.8	6.2
Fucose	0.3	0.2	0.7
Hexosamine	1.1	3.8	3.3
Sialic acid	0.2	1.7	2.0
Total	2.8	10.5	12.2

(From Cohen and Porter (1964), Table V. See reference for additional data and sources.)

TABLE 4

Amino Acid Composition of Rabbit and Horse IgG

Amino Acid	Light Chains		Heavy Chains	
	Rabbit	Horse	Rabbit	Horse
	residues/20,000 gm		*residues/50,000 gm*	
Lysine	8	10	23	26
Histidine	2	2	7	10
Arginine	3	4	16	10
Aspartic acid	16	12	33	30
Threonine	25	17	49	37
Serine	19	28	49	45
Glutamic acid	18	16	40	38
Proline	10	11	36	31
Glycine	15	16	33	28
Alanine	13	12	24	22
Valine	18	14	41	46
Methionine	0.9	0.8	5	4
Isoleucine	6	10	15	13
Leucine	11	11	30	28
Tyrosine	10	6	17	16
Phenylalanine	5	4	14	13
Half-cystine	6	3	10	3
S-Carboxymethylcysteine	1	1	4	3 (4?)
Tryptophan	4	3	8	8

(From Cohen and Porter (1964), Tables III and IV. See reference for additional data.)

somewhat. However, the relative differences between IgG and the other two are outside the range of expected variation and represent true class distinctiveness.

The analysis of comparable rabbit and horse immunoglobulins reveals considerable over-all uniformity with the human globulin and some striking differences (Table 4), such as in the threonine content of rabbit IgG. Carbohydrate content of the globulin is comparable to human IgG.

Physico-chemical properties, already shown in their relation to other serum components in Chapter 2, are given in summary in Table 5 for the three major classes of human immunoglobulins. As emphasized previously and reiterated once more, these properties are only suggestive and may be expected to vary operationally from one preparation to the next. Even if determined with extreme precision for an individual preparation of high purity (such as the 137,000 given for the molecular weight of rabbit IgG by Cammack, 1962), slightly different values might result from exacting analyses of other individual preparations. When the limits

TABLE 5

Physico-Chemical Properties of Human Immunoglobulin

Properties	IgG	IgA	IgM
f/f_0	1.38	1.38	1.73
Molecular weight	160,000	$(160,000)_{1,2,4}$	$(160,000)_{6,8,}$ ...
s_{20}^0	6.6	6.6, 10, 13	19, 26, 32, ...
s_{20} in mercaptoethanol	6.6	6.6	6.6
μ, pH 8.6, $\Gamma/2 = 0.1$	1.1*	1.2–3.6	0.5–2.3
pI	6.2–8.5	4.8–6.5	5.5–7.4
In normal serum (gm%)	1.2	0.1–0.4	0.1

(From Putnam, 1965, p. 231. See reference for additional data and original sources.)

* Average value.

of heterogeneity are finally established, exacting analyses within those limits will have greater meaning and usefulness.

Putnam (1965) has stated that "the single most frustrating obstacle to establishing a coherent model for the structure of the γ-globulins of various species has been the inability to obtain consistent stoichiometric values for the N-terminal groups." Whether it is heterogeneity of chemical structure or technical inability to detect amino end groups consistently, the apparent impasse results in an inability to determine the number of polypeptide chains contained in the intact immunoglobulins with certainty. A summary of knowledge concerning N-terminal amino acids of IgG from a number of species in Table 6 reveals that only rabbit IgG is satisfactorily consistent with 1.0 mole of alanine per mole of protein. Even in this case submolar quantities of aspartic acid have been found. The near molar equivalents of aspartic and glutamic acids in human globulin suggest two major chains, and the fact that the relative proportion of these varies from preparation to preparation suggests that the chains may be on separate protein molecules at least in some cases. One mole of N-terminal alanine and two of glutamic acid in pig IgG indicate further heterogeneity. Most distressing to the protein chemist are the analyses for bovine and equine N-terminal groups, which not only show multiplicity but also fail to yield in total amount an average of even one N-terminal group per globulin molecule. Blockage of free amino groups must occur in these situations as well as heterogeneity.

The C-terminal ends of bovine IgG are in greater abundance with 1 mole per mole of protein attributable to serine and glycine. In rabbit IgG there are 4 moles per mole distributed among glycine, serine, alanine, and threonine in a ratio of 4:2:1:1. Human IgG appears to have glycine

TABLE 6

The N-Terminal Amino Acids of IgG from Different Species

Amino Acid	Species				
	Human	Horse	Cow	Pig	Rabbit
			moles/mole globulin		
Alanine....................		0.0–0.44	0.09–0.12	1.0	0.9–1.1
Aspartic acid..............	0.9–1.1	0.15–0.23	0.13–0.23		0.2–0.4
Glutamic acid..............	0.9–1.8	0.09–0.18	0.06–0.15	2.0	
Leucine....................		0.08–0.17			
Serine.....................	0.1	0.09–0.16	0.09–0.14		
Valine.....................		0.0–0.18	0.11–0.35		
Total.....................	1.8–3.0	0.4–1.19	0.57–0.87	3.0	1.0–1.4

(From Putnam (1965) p. 235, and Singer (1965), p. 279. See references for additional data and original sources.)

and serine in C-terminal positions. Once again, however, biological variescence is indicated.

The pathological globulins (myeloma and macroglobulins) provide an even better indication of heterogeneity with respect to N-terminal amino acid assay. A globulin of a particular type is produced in abnormally high amounts and results in greater homogeneity in the individual preparation. On the other hand, from one individual to the next, extensive heterogeneity is exhibited, indicating that there is no representative structure that can be taken as a model. Normal serum without a doubt would be found to contain small amounts of each of the homogeneous abnormal types. Putnam (1965) lists six structural types found in 94 pathological myeloma and macroglobulin cases:

No N-terminal group
N-terminal aspartic acid only
N-terminal glutamic acid only
N-terminal aspartic and glutamic acids only
N-terminal groups formed with monocarboxylic amino acids (leucine, tyrosine, threonine, or serine) but not dicarboxylic amino acids
A miscellany of N-terminal groups

The dicarboxylic acids occurred as N-terminal groups in over half of the cases. Molar proportions were distributed as shown in Table 7.

Inherent in the nomenclature suggested by the WHO signatories for human immunoglobulins is the assumption of four-chain models. The assumption arises from extensive studies of cleavage products of the

TABLE 7

N-Terminal Groups of Pathological Globulins

N-Terminal Groups	Number of Specimens	
	Myeloma	Macroglobulin
Aspartic acid		
0.5-1.5 moles..........................	8	6
1.7–2.5 moles..........................	9	1
Glutamic acid		
0.8–1.5 moles..........................	2	11
1.7–2.3 moles..........................	6	0
2.9–3.5 moles..........................	4	1
Aspartic and glutamic acids...............	18	9
All others..............................	17	2
Total specimens.......................	64	30

(Constructed from Putnam, 1965, p. 237. See reference for histogram and original sources.)

immunoglobulins from a number of species, particularly from rabbit IgG, and from studies on dissociated fragments that reassociate to form fairly intact immunoglobulins. The assumption is probably a sage one to make, but the wide-ranging results of terminal amino acid assays cannot give support to the models. Instead, a certain amount of discomfort is provided by those assays, enough to prevent the operational structural models from becoming definitive.

Heterogeneity within the immunoglobulins has hampered satisfactory terminal amino acid assays. It has also prevented crystallization by which structural models could be built via X-ray diffraction data. Only optical rotatory dispersion and infrared spectrophotometric measurements have so far added further physical dimensions to the established ellipsoidal nature of globulins in solution. Jirgensons (1960) found that all natural state γ-globulins had low dispersion constants which he interpreted as indicating little helical formation. Winkler and Doty (1961) gave confirmation to this interpretation from infrared analysis, failing to find bands characteristic of either α- or β-helices. Imahori and Momoi (1962) also looked for but did not find indications of helix formation. To account for a folded 7S molecule with major and minor axes, respectively, of 235 Å and 44 Å (Oncley, Scatchard, and Brown, 1947), without invoking helical formation and the hydrogen bonding associated with it, there is little else to assume but that hydrophobic bonding is predominant.

In view of the lack of physical definition of the intact proteins it is indeed remarkable that an international group of 14 scientists could ever put forth a definition and nomenclature of the immunoglobulins. The thread that gave unanimity to their decision was not through considerations of gross structure, however, but through interpretation of data obtained with immunoglobulin fragments. As revealed in the next chapter, the unifying thread was for the most part immunochemical, and their unanimity attained by way of this thread in itself attests to the power of the immunochemical method.

REFERENCES

Cammack, K. A. (1962). Molecular weight of rabbit gamma-globulin. Nature *194:* 745–747.

Ceppellini, R., Dray, S., Edelman, G., Fahey, J., Franěk, F., Franklin, E., Goodman, H. C., Grabar, P., Gurvich, A. E., Heremans, J. F., Isliker, H., Karush, F., Press, E., and Trnka, Z. (1964). Nomenclature for human immunoglobulins. Bull. World Health Organ. *30:* 447–450; Immunochemistry *1:* 145–149.

Cohen, S., and Porter, R. R. (1964). Structural and biological activity of immunoglobulins. Advan. Immunol. *4:* 287–349.

Imahori, K., and Momoi, H. (1962). Globulin and myeloma: the structural characterization of γ-globulin and myeloma protein. Arch. Biochem. Biophys. *97:* 236–242.

Jirgensons, B. (1960). Optical rotatory properties of some abnormal serum globulins. Arch. Biochem. Biophys. *89:* 48–52.

Oncley, J. L., Scatchard, G., and Brown, A. (1947). Physical-chemical characteristics of certain of the proteins of normal human plasma. J. Phys. Colloid Chem. *51:* 184–198.

Putnam, F. W. (1965). Structure and function of the plasma proteins. In *The Proteins*, 2nd Ed., Vol. III, Neurath, H., ed., Academic Press (New York, pp. 153–267), p. 234.

Rowe, D. S., and Fahey, J. L. (1965). A new class of human immunoglobulins. I. A unique myeloma protein. II. Normal serum IgD. J. Exptl. Med. *121:* 171–199.

Singer, S. J. (1965). Structure and function of antigen and antibody proteins. In *The Proteins*, 2nd Ed., Vol. III, Neurath, H., ed., Academic Press (New York, pp. 269–357), p. 279.

Winkler, M. J., and Doty, P. (1961). Some observations on the configuration and precipitating activity of antibodies. Biochim. Biophys. Acta *54:* 448–454.

WHO Committee (1964). (See Ceppellini *et al.*)

4

The Fragments of Immunoglobulins

1. Naturally occurring fragments

In 1845 Professor H. Bence Jones, an English pathologist, received a letter from Dr. Watson, a general practitioner, which described an accompanying urine specimen that was obtained from a patient suffering from *mollities ossium*. The letter was short and to the point:

Saturday, Nov. 1st, 1845

Dear Dr. Jones,—The tube contains urine of very high specific gravity. When boiled it becomes slightly opaque. On the addition of nitric acid, it effervesces, assumes a reddish hue, and becomes quite clear; but as it cools, assumes the consistence and appearance which you see. Heat reliquefies it. What is it?

(Signed) DR. WATSON

Jones (1847) analyzed the specimen and found it to contain a protein substance (an "oxide of albumen") that was distinguishable from albumin by its solubility in nitric acid and lack of heat coagulability. After separation by precipitation with alcohol the protein retained its characteristics of solubility in cold water, increased solubility in boiling water, coagulation with continued boiling, and return to solution by even further boiling. The substance could then be precipitated with acid, solubilized by heating, and reprecipitated by cooling. Jones noted at the end of his analysis: "Each oz. of this urine contained as much nutritive matter as an oz. of the blood. No supply of food could compensate for such a loss."

Through the years other clinicians found such urinary proteins from time to time that exhibited the same solubility characteristics as this one and the name *Bence-Jones proteins* was appended to them. In diag-

41

nosing cases for multiple myeloma, analysis of urine for Bence-Jones protein became routine because of the high association between the plasma-cell disease and the urinary pattern. Another characteristic of multiple myeloma was the unusually high degree of increased plasma protein levels (hyperproteinemia), unequivocally shown in 1928 by Perlzweig, Delrue, and Geschickter. The increase in protein was later shown due mainly to globulins with β- and γ-mobility (e.g., in the study by Moore, Kabat, and Gutman, 1943), as well as in components similar to urinary Bence-Jones protein (cf. review by Gutman, 1948).

Physico-chemical characterization of Bence-Jones proteins developed at the same time as characterization of plasma components, but the large degree of variation exhibited by individual results from different laboratories and/or from individual patients led Putnam and Stelos (1953) to explore the reasons for such divergence. Mobilities, sedimentation coefficients, and diffusion coefficients were determined with extreme precision for 18 different cases of multiple myeloma, but, in spite of the care taken, extreme heterogeneity was observed. Mobilities ranged from 1.0 to 6.9; sedimentation coefficients, 2.05 to 6.30; isoelectric points, 4.6 to 6.7. There was no pattern except diversity itself—and the common peculiar property first noted by Professor Jones, that of precipitating when slowly heated, redissolving on boiling, and reprecipitating when cooled (Putnam, Easley, Lynn, Ritchie, and Phelps, 1959).

Then, in 1955, came the beginning of a solution. Through application of Ouchterlony's new agar-gel diffusion technique for measuring antigen-antibody reactions (1953), Korngold and Lipari (1955) and Deutsch, Kratochvil, and Reif (1955) established the immunochemical relationship between the relatively small molecules of Bence-Jones proteins (molecular weight of about 40,000), the myeloma immunoglobulins, and normal IgG.

Hektoen as early as 1921 had investigated the immunological properties of specific precipitates formed between antibody and Bence-Jones proteins, and Baynes-Jones and Wilson in that same year had established two different groups on the basis of antigenic specificity. Hektoen and Welker (1940) showed that these two groups could appear at times in the urine of the same patient. Yet 34 years passed before the relationship with serum globulin was established! Korngold and Lipari in 1956 treated the immunological relationship between the urinary microglobulins and normal and myeloma γ-globulins in depth and demonstrated three types, two later identified with IgG and the other with IgA. In 1958 Webb, Rose, and Sehon succeeded in immunochemically identifying the microglobulins in normal urine, thus removing Bence-Jones proteins from the category of myeloma specificity, and in 1961 Berggard identified them in normal plasma.

Meanwhile other immunochemical events, to be detailed later on in the chapter, were converging. Beginning with the separation of sub-units of IgG into light and heavy chains by Edelman (1959), subsequent events showed that Bence-Jones microglobulins and the light chains from IgG were very similar. Poulik and Edelman (1961), by alkylating reduced light chains to prevent them from recombining, and by re-ducing and alkylating Bence-Jones microglobulins in a similar way, showed that as long as the source of the reduced proteins was from the same patient a common electrophoretic mobility was obtained. Edelman and Galley (1962) then proceeded to demonstrate exquisitely that the light chains from normal IgG exhibited the same peculiar thermal properties that H. Bence Jones had originally observed in 1845 with Dr. Watson's urine specimen!

Reinforcing their views by observing similarities in amino acid anal-ysis of light chains and urinary microglobulins from the same patient, and obtaining homogeneity in ion-exchange chromatography of the two on CM-cellulose, Edelman and Galley concluded that Bence-Jones proteins were, in fact, polymeric forms of light chains with dimers of 40,000 molecular weight predominating. In terms of the WHO nomen-clature the two antigenically distinct types of microglobulins, as dimers of light chains, would be written as κ_2 and λ_2.

It can be expected that other examples of incomplete globulins will be found, and it will be an exercise for immunobiologists and immu-nopathologists to determine whether the naturally occurring fragments in any particular instance result from incomplete synthesis of immu-noglobulins, degradation of previously formed immunoglobulins, or, possibly, a dynamic equilibrium between fragments and whole products.

A clear-cut example of the existence of another type of naturally occurring immunoglobulin fragment is found in the work of Franěk and Říha (1964), already alluded to in Chapter 2. These Czech scientists found a 5S fragment of immunoglobulin in the new-born serum of co-lostrum-free piglets. Since the fragment was in low concentration in the serum there was great difficulty in obtaining enough for complete studies, but peptide-fingerprinting techniques revealed a number of interesting points.

Previously, Putnam (1962) had very effectively shown by two-di-mensional chromatographic and electrophoretic separation of peptides from tryptic digests of Bence-Jones microglobulins that the "fingerprints" thus obtained were closely similar to the "fingerprints" of a subunit portion of myeloma or normal globulins obtained from the same individual. Unlike fingerprint heterogeneity that had been displayed from one individual to the next, structural identity by chemical means was now established for the first time between the naturally occurring light-chain fragment and its counterpart in whole globulin in a given individual. Schwartz and Edelman (1963) then showed that peptide maps of separated light chains from 6.5S myeloma globulin and those of naturally occurring Bence-Jones light chains from the same individual were similar.

Franěk and Říha (1964) compared the peptide maps of their 5S piglet globulin with those of intact pig IgG and found several discrepancies. However, when they compared the 5S fingerprints with those of light- and heavy-chain fragments from IgG, they found no correspondence at all with light-chain fingerprints but did find a very close resemblance to the heavy-chain pattern. Even in view of heterogeneity which accounted for certain differences in the latter (since pooled 5S components from several new-borns were needed to provide enough material), the resemblance was more than suggestive (Fig. 14). In keeping with the WHO system of nomenclature, antigenic analysis would be required to determine the type of heavy chain represented by the 5S globulin, but, for example, if it were found that the component were similar to IgG heavy chains, it would be designated as γ_2.

Reports of "heavy chain" disease in the human have been made (Franklin, Lowenstein, Bigelow, and Meltzer, 1964), but the fragments found do not correspond with complete heavy chains. They have a greater similarity to the enzymatically cleaved heavy-chain piece, the crystallizable fragment, that is discussed later on. If this be so then the piglet 5S globulin would be referred to according to the nomenclature as Fc.

2. Fragments obtained by reduction

Unlike many proteins the immunoglobulins were found to resist dissociation into smaller units by the usual procedures of treatment with 8 M urea, guanidine hydrochloride, and other agents which effected breakage of non-covalent bonds. Their resistance to this type of denaturation was well exemplified by an experiment of Karush (1962) in which an antihapten antibody was subjected to treatment with 8 M urea. After the urea was subsequently removed by dialysis the immunoglobulin returned to its near native globular form, and its antibody re-

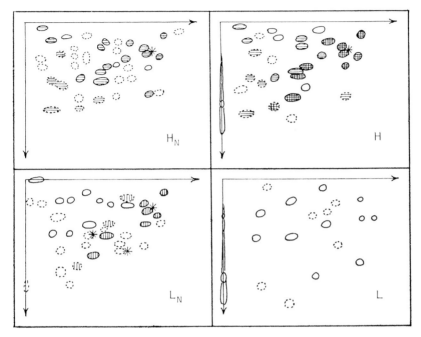

Fig. 14. Peptide maps of subunits of 5S γ-globulin from new-born pig serum. Electrophoretic separations are shown *horizontally;* chromatographic separations, *vertically.* H_N and L_N are heavy- and light-chain subunits of the 5S globulin; H and L are heavy- and light-chain subunits of 7S γ-globulin. Peptides common to the two sources of heavy chains are *horizontally hatched;* peptides common to the two sources of light chains are *vertically hatched. Asterisks* mark peptides that stained yellow with ninhydrin. (Franěk and Říha, 1964.)

activity, which had been lost during urea exposure, was nearly completely regained.

Yet the work of Putnam (1953) had indicated from N-terminal amino acid analyses (regardless of the heterogeneity involved) that an immunoglobulin must not be just one long polypeptide chain, compactly folded, but rather must be constructed in multichain fashion. Edelman (1959), hypothesizing that there were indeed chains held together by disulfide bonds but that unfolding of the protein molecule was necessary to expose them, subjected human IgG to the double treatment of unfolding in 6 M urea and reduction of disulfide linkages with mercaptoethanol. Fragments with an average molecular weight of 50,000 were obtained and Putnam's conclusion was thereby supported. In quick order a variety of human and animal immunoglobulins were treated with chemical cleavage reagents with similar results (Franěk, 1961; Edelman and Poulik, 1961; Phelps, Neet, Lynn, and Putnam, 1961). The final result was the isolation of pairs of light and heavy polypeptide chains of which the light, as described above, had a community of properties in common with Bence-Jones proteins.

A problem to be resolved was the number of disulfide bridges connecting the various chains. After complete reductions of all S—S bonds in rabbit IgG, for example, a total of 44 sulfhydryl groups were found (Porter, 1959; Markus, Grossberg, and Pressman, 1962), which would make possible as many as $44!/22! \, 2^{22}$ or 5.6×10^{26} different disulfide linkages if these were random. For rabbit IgG, Palmer, Nisonoff, and Van Holde (1963) were able to cleave the molecule into only two subunits of equal size. Reduction was accomplished with 0.1 M 2-mercaptoethylamine and separation was maintained by lowering the pH to 2.5 in 0.1 M NaCl. The agreement between weight- and number-average molecular weights of the subunit preparation, its homogeneity in the ultracentrifuge, and a very low yield of light chains all strongly indicated that dissociation into half-molecules had been accomplished. Of even greater importance was the fact that when the reduced, acidified preparation was returned to neutral pH, and recombinations of the subunits through restoration of disulfide bridges were thus accomplished, the recombination obviously did not take place randomly. The major product in the restored preparation had physico-chemical characteristics of the untreated native protein. If recombination had been random there would not have been such remarkable renaturation. When an antihapten antibody was subjected to this treatment, it retained its specific combining capacity, again reinforcing the concept that half-molecule recombination into whole molecules involved a very specific type of disulfide bond.

Palmer and Nisonoff (1964) investigated this type of dissociation in greater detail and discovered that within the normal IgG of individual rabbits about one-half to two-thirds of the molecules could be split in half after the reduction of only one very labile disulfide bond. The remaining molecules could be split in half only by further reduction, an indication of heterogeneity in intrachain disulfide bridging. The amino acid content of the split products was identical to that of the whole protein and was also consistent with the concept that each half-molecule was composed of a light and heavy chain. Furthermore, the work substantiated a former concept that the single labile disulfide bond (as well as each of the less easily reduced multiple bridges in some of the molecules) was a link between two heavy chains.

3. Enzymatic cleavage followed by reduction

Further resolution of the problem of disulfide bridging between the multiple chains of immunoglobulins is found in reports concerning the effect of reduction upon subunits obtained not by chemical processes but by limited enzymatic digestion.

Historically, the treatment of immunoglobulins with proteolytic enzymes preceded treatment with reducing agents by a number of years. The results were highly varied and the reports conflicting (Marrack, 1938). Retention of antibody function was the only measurable quantity that was generally assayed. One important conclusion was drawn from the early work, however—that a relatively short and limited exposure to an enzyme such as pepsin could result in partial digestion without loss of antibody combining capacity. This idea was incorporated into Parfentjev's patented pepsin process (1936) for preparing a horse diphtheria antitoxin that would still be potent but would, by loss of certain protein parts, be less antigenic in humans in whom it was administered. Pope (1938, 1939), who developed a similar process, incorporated not only short-term pepsin digestion but also selective heat denaturation of the cleaved products at an acid pH in the presence of ammonium sulfate. He observed that two types of protein were obtained, one non-antitoxic and easily heat-coagulable, the other antitoxic and heat-stable.

Porter (1950) had obtained a fragment of rabbit antibody against egg albumin by papain digestion which, although it had lost precipitating activity, would bind with egg albumin and block precipitation of the albumin by whole antibody. The fragment had an average molecular weight of 40,000. With the advent of crystalline papain and the improvement in fractionation procedures Porter returned to this system in 1958 and found that he could now control the splitting process, separate the fragments, and analyze the products (Porter, 1958, 1959).

He prepared rabbit IgG from several different antisera, digested the proteins with papain (using cysteine as an enzyme activator), and separated the fragments via CM-cellulose ion-exchange chromatography. The profile of the effluent from the ion-exchange column revealed three sharp peaks which were designated I, II, and III in order of their appearance. Immunological reactivity was confined to I and II as shown by inhibition of precipitation of antigens. Dialysis of the fragments against distilled water at 2°C resulted in a crystalline precipitate of Fraction III. Molecular weight studies showed that Fragment I was about 50,000; II, 53,000; III, 80,000; and the intact IgG, 188,000.

Confirmation of this significant work came quickly (Nisonoff and Woernley, 1959) and, shortly thereafter, an explanation of mode of action (Nisonoff, Wissler, Lipman, and Woernley, 1960). In Porter's hands (1950) only papain had the property of yielding split products with retention of precipitin-blocking activity. Nisonoff, noting that cysteine was generally used in conjunction with papain as activator, turned to the action of pepsin upon antibody and found that he could produce a 5S bivalent antibody fragment, and that the 5S fragment would in turn split into two univalent 3.5S fragments upon the application of cysteine. The 5S fragment, although reduced in molecular weight from the natural state to 100,000, retained its capacity to precipitate antigen (which, as will be shown later, depends on two combining sites). The 3.5S fragments, like those of Porter's Fractions I and II, would block but not precipitate, and represented fragments with single combining sites. The univalent fragments would also recombine to give a bivalent product (Nisonoff, Wissler, and Lipman, 1960).

It was clear from a study of this work and that of Palmer and Nisonoff (1964) cited above that the single labile disulfide bond that joined the two halves of rabbit IgG was also the bond that joined the two univalent fragments. Since reductions alone (and subsequent dissociation in acid) resulted in two symmetrical fragments that were univalent with respect to antibody activity whereas enzyme cleavage alone resulted in two asymmetrical fragments, one of which retained full bivalency, and since, further, the bivalent fragment could be symmetrically cleaved into two small univalent fragments, a structural model could be constructed in which the plane of symmetry of chemical cleavage was sectioned by a plane of asymmetrical enzyme cleavage.

4. The linkage between heavy and light chains

Although at first it was felt that Fragments I and II were not antigenic and that Fragment III carried the antigenic determinants that made possible the immunization of one species with IgG from another, Putnam, Tan, Lynn, Easley, and Migita (1962) showed that each fragment carried partial determinants of the whole. Fleischman, Porter, and Press (1963) finally discovered the actual relationship between the enzyme Fragments I and II and the light chains of IgG found originally by Edelman. This required obtaining light chains that would be soluble in aqueous solution rather than those obtained in urea, which were insoluble when urea was removed. By reducing IgG in urea-free solutions and separating the resultant chains on Sephadex-75 in the presence of weak acids (1 N acetic or propionic), Fleischman et al. (1963) obtained in nearly 100 % yield two fractions representing light and heavy chains. This same system, when applied to Fragments I and II, gave rise to intact light

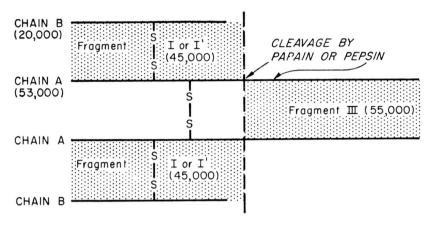

CHAIN B (20,000)

CHAIN A (53,000)

CHAIN A

CHAIN B

Fragment I or I' (45,000)

CLEAVAGE BY PAPAIN OR PEPSIN

Fragment III (55,000)

Fragment I or I' (45,000)

FIG. 15. Possible arrangement of polypeptide chains in rabbit IgG. (Nisonoff and Thorbecke, 1964.)

chains and only a fragment of heavy-chain material. The linkage of the light chain to the heavy chain was shown to be that of a single disulfide bond.

From these data a chain model of IgG structure was constructed by Fleischman *et al.* (1963) and modified by Nisonoff and Thorbecke (1964). The model (Fig. 15) shows two heavy chains joined by one labile disulfide bond and further bound by non-covalent forces as well as, in some instances, by additional S—S bonds. The labile S—S bond lies to one side of the plane of enzymatic cleavage whereas the other bonds lie on the other. Bound to each heavy chain by a single S—S bond is a light chain whose point of attachment is somewhere near the S—S bond joining the two heavy chains and on the same side of the plane of enzymatic cleavage.

The initial findings of the two fragments, I and II, in Porter's papain digest could have been interpreted two ways: either I and II appeared in the same naturally occurring molecule or they came from separate molecules as pairs of one or the other. The work of Amiraian and Leikhim (1961), which was confirmed by Palmer, Mandy, and Nisonoff (1962), indicated that the latter was true and that I and II resulted from heterogeneous populations of globulin molecules.

With regard to N-terminal amino acids, alanine and aspartic acid in rabbit IgG were found associated with the light chains (Fleischman *et al.*, 1963). The carbohydrate moiety, on the other hand, was found joined to the heavy chains and principally in Fragment III.

5. Antigenic relationships among fragments

Although the arrangement of the four chains in rabbit IgG can be acceptably taken as shown in the model, direct evidence for a similar situation in human and mouse IgG is not so clear-cut, and inferences must be drawn, many of them from immunochemical data, to permit analogous models of IgG from other species to be constructed. The problem in each case comes in the placement of the disulfide bridges, in the exploration of disulfide bond heterogeneity, in the fortuitous or deliberate finding of single labile bonds, and, finally, in the determination of the plane of enzymatic cleavage with respect to these bridges. The results of antigenic analysis of fragments permit construction of these analogues.

For example, when Askonas and Fahey (1962) produced subunits of mouse myeloma IgA by papain cleavage, they obtained two fractions, one (S) with an electrophoretic mobility slower than the other (F). Upon comparison of the two fragments and whole IgA in agar-gel double diffusion with respect to their reaction with an antiserum against mouse IgA, it was found (Fig. 16) that Fragments S and F were antigenically distinct; also that the S fragment formed an antigenic community with the mouse equivalent of Bence-Jones protein and with mouse IgG whereas the F fragment differed antigenically from those two sources of light chains. Thus it seemed evident that enzymatic cleavage had produced the equivalent of the fragments obtained with digestion of rabbit IgG, one rich in light-chain material, the other in heavy. In the same way Fahey and Askonas (1962) subjected mouse IgG to papain digestion, found S and F fragments, and established that the S fragment was the carrier of antibody activity.

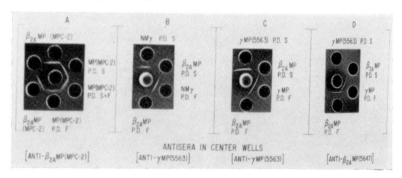

FIG. 16. Characterization of mouse IgA from myeloma MPC-2 serum. F fragments were partially separated from S fragments. β_{2A} means IgA; $P.D.$ means papain digest; NM_γ means normal mouse γ-globulin; MP means myeloma protein. (Askonas and Fahey, 1962.)

Papain cleavage of human IgG had earlier been shown to give rise to two fractions (Edelman, Heremans, Heremans, and Kunkel, 1960) with S and F relative mobilities and with distinct antigenic differences as shown by agar-gel immunoelectrophoresis. Franklin and Stanworth (1961) established the antigenic relationship between the S fragment and Bence-Jones protein, thereby conferring upon the S the light-chain moiety and upon the F the heavy.

To designate the fragments by some nomenclature, the WHO committee selected the following terms: Fab-fragment, Fc-fragment, and Fd-fragment. Fab-fragment would include Porter's Fractions I and II, S pieces, and univalent antibody fragments. The 5S bivalent fragment would be called $(Fab)_2$. The Fc-fragment would be that portion of heavy chains, frequently crystallizable, that contained no activity. Fd would be that part of the heavy chain associated with Fab (which Fleischman, Porter, and Press had called the "A piece"). It is not clear whether Fc should refer to a dimeric or monomeric piece of heavy chain. The fragment found by Franklin et al. (1964), which was associated with "heavy-chain" disease, had a close similarity to Fc with a molecular weight of 51,000 but it could be dissociated into two half-molecules by reduction and alkylation, and each half was designated Fc (Franklin, 1964).

6. Position of allotypes

Isoantigenic determinants in rabbit IgG that resulted in the production of anti-IgG in other rabbits were discovered by Oudin (1956). It was found in subsequent studies by Oudin (1960), by Dray and Young (1958), and by Dubiski, Dudziak, Skalba, and Dubiska (1959) that the isoantigens were genetically controlled and subject to genetic segregation. It was established in later work (Dubiski, Dubiska, Skalba, and Kelus, 1961; Marrack, Richards, and Kelus, 1961; Leskowitz, 1963) that the allotypic specificities were present on the Fab-fragments, but not on Fc-fragments to any great extent, if at all. Finally the report of Gilman, Nisonoff, and Dray (1964) confirmed the lack of allotypic isoantigens on rabbit Fc-fragments and demonstrated that they were symmetrically divided between the two Fab-fragments of rabbit IgG. The use of such genetic markers in rabbit immunoglobulins further substantiated the model as given.

Interestingly enough, however, the locale of similar genetic markers in human immunoglobulins was found to be differently placed. The Gm allotypes discovered by Grubb (1956) were found associated with the Fc-fragment of IgG, were specific for γ-heavy chains, and therefore did not appear in IgA or IgM (Franklin, Fudenberg, Meltzer, and Stanworth, 1962; Harboe, Osterland, and Kunkel, 1962; Martensson, 1961; Fahey and Lawler, 1961). The InV determinants of Ropartz, Lenoir, and Rivat (1961), on the other hand, were found to be associated with Fab-fragments and with Bence-Jones proteins (Fudenberg and Franklin, 1963). The κ-light chains were found to be InV positive and the λ-chains InV negative in IgA.

The Fc-fragments that were found in the heavy-chain disease reported by Franklin *et al.* (1964) and by Osserman and Takatsuki (1964) were found to contain the Gm determinants and therefore could be classified as γ-chain fragments.

The position of the allotypic antigens therefore forms an important marker for further establishment of immunoglobulin structure. It provides another immunochemical means of determining chain identity in the midst of structural heterogeneity.

REFERENCES

Amiraian, K., and Leikhim, E. J. (1961). Preparation and properties of antibodies to sheep erythrocytes. J. Immunol. 87: 301–309.

Askonas, B. A., and Fahey, J. L. (1962). Enzymatically produced subunits of proteins formed by plasma cells in mice. II. β_{2A}-myeloma protein and Bence-Jones protein. J. Exptl. Med. 115: 641–653.

Baynes-Jones, S., and Wilson, D. W. (1921). Specific immunological reactions of Bence-Jones proteins. Proc. Soc. Exptl. Biol. Med. 18: 220–222.

Berggard, I. (1961). On a γ-globulin of low molecular weight in normal human plasma and urine. Clin. Chim. Acta 6: 545–549.

Deutsch, H. F., Kratochvil, C. H., and Reif, A. G. (1955). Immunochemical relation of Bence-Jones proteins to normal serum proteins. J. Biol. Chem. 216: 103–111.

Dray, S., and Young, G. O. (1958). Differences in the antigenic components of sera of individual rabbits as shown by induced isoprecipitins. J. Immunol. 81: 142–149.

Dubiski, S., Dubiska, A., Skalba, D., and Kelus, A. (1961). Antigenic structure of rabbit gamma-globulin. Immunology 4: 236–243.

Dubiski, S., Dudziak, Z., Skalba, D., and Dubiska, A. (1959). Serum groups in rabbits. Immunology 2: 84–92.

Edelman, G. A. (1959). Dissociation of γ-globulin. J. Am. Chem. Soc. 81: 3155–3156.

Edelman, G. M., and Galley, J. A. (1962). The nature of Bence-Jones proteins. Chemical similarities to polypeptide chains of myeloma globulins and normal γ-globulins. J. Exptl. Med. 116: 207–227.

Edelman, G. M., Heremans, J. F., Heremans, M.-T., and Kunkel, H. G. (1960). Immunological studies of human γ-globulin. Relation of the precipitin lines of whole γ-globulin to those of the fragments produced by papain. J. Exptl. Med. 112: 203–223.

Edelman, G. M., and Poulik, M. D. (1961). Studies on the structural units of the γ-globulins. J. Exptl. Med. 113: 861–884.

Fahey, J. L., and Askonas, B. A. (1962). Enzymatically produced subunits of proteins formed by plasma cells in mice. I. γ-Globulin and γ-myeloma proteins. J. Exptl. Med. *115:* 623–639.

Fahey, J. L., and Lawler, S. D. (1961). Gm factors in normal γ-globulin fraction, myeloma proteins, and macroglobulins. J. Natl. Cancer Inst. *27:* 973–981.

Fleischman, J. B., Porter, R. R., and Press, E. M. (1963). The arrangement of the peptide chains in γ-globulin. Biochem. J. *88:* 220–228.

Franěk, F. (1961). Dissociation of animal 7S γ-globulins by cleavage of disulfide bonds. Biochem. Biophys. Res. Commun. *4:* 28–32.

Franěk, F., and Říha, I. (1964). Purification and structural characterization of 5S γ-globulin in new-born pigs. Immunochemistry *1:* 49–63.

Franklin, E. C. (1964). Structural studies of human 7S γ-globulin (G immunoglobulin). Further observations of a naturally occurring protein related to the crystallizable (fast) fragment. J. Exptl. Med. *120:* 691–709.

Franklin, E. C., Fudenberg, H., Meltzer, M., and Stanworth, D. R. (1962). The structural basis for genetic variations of normal human γ-globulins. Proc. Natl. Acad. Sci. U. S. *48:* 914–922.

Franklin, E. C., Lowenstein, J., Bigelow, B., and Meltzer, M. (1964). Heavy chain disease—a new disorder of serum γ-globulins. Report of the first case. Am. J. Med. *37:* 332–350.

Franklin, E. C., and Stanworth, D. R. (1961). Antigenic relationships between immune globulins and certain related paraproteins in man. J. Exptl. Med. *114:* 521–533.

Fudenberg, J., and Franklin, E. C. (1963). Genetic control and its relation to disease. Ann. Internal Med. *58:* 171–180.

Gilman, A. M., Nisonoff, A., and Dray, S. (1964). Symmetrical distribution of genetic markers in individual rabbit gamma globulin molecules. Immunochemistry *1:* 109–120.

Grubb, R. (1956). Agglutination of erythrocytes coated with "incomplete" anti-RH by certain rheumatoid arthritic sera and some other sera. Acta Pathol. Microbiol. Scand. *39:* 195–197.

Gutman, A. B. (1948). The plasma proteins in disease. Advan. Protein Chem. *4:* 155–250.

Harboe, M., Osterland, C. K., and Kunkel, H. G. (1962). Localization of two genetic factors to different areas of γ-globulin molecules. Science *136:* 979–980.

Hektoen, L. (1921). Specific precipitin for Bence-Jones protein. J. Am. Med. Assoc. *76:* 929–930.

Hektoen, L., and Welker, W. H. (1940). Immunological differences of crystalline Bence-Jones proteins. Biochem. J. *34:* 487–489.

Jones, H. Bence (1847). Papers on chemical pathology, Lecture III. Lancet *2:* 88–92.

Karush, F. (1962). The role of disulfide bonds in the acquisition of immunologic specificity. J. Pediat. *60:* 103–113.

Korngold, L., and Lipari, R. (1955). Immunological studies of Bence-Jones proteins. Proc. Am. Assoc. Cancer Res. *2:* 29–30.

Korngold, L., and Lipari, R. (1956). Multiple-myeloma proteins. I. Immunological studies. Cancer *9:* 183–192.

Leskowitz, S. (1963). Immunochemical study of rabbit γ-globulin allotypes. J. Immunol. *90:* 98–106.

Markus, G., Grossberg, A. L., and Pressman, D. (1962). The disulfide bonds of rabbit γ-globulin and its fragments. Arch. Biochem. Biophys. *96:* 63–69.

Marrack, J. R. (1938). *The Chemistry of Antigens and Antibodies*. His Majesty's Printing Office, (London, 194 pp.), pp. 52–53.

Marrack, J. R., Richards, C. B., and Kelus, A. (1961). Antigenic specificity of hydrolysis products of γ-globulins. Protides Biol. Fluids *9:* 200–206.

Martensson, L. (1961). Gm characters of m-components. Acta Med. Scand., Suppl. *367:* 87–93.

Moore, D. H., Kabat, E. A., and Gutman, A. B. (1943). Bence-Jones proteinemia in multiple myeloma. J. Clin. Invest. *22:* 67–75.

Nisonoff, A., and Thorbecke, G. J. (1964). Immunochemistry. Ann. Rev. Biochem. *33:* 355–402.

Nisonoff, A., Wissler, F. C., and Lipman, L. N. (1960). Properties of the major component of a peptic digest of rabbit antibody. Science *132:* 1770–1771.

Nisonoff, A., Wissler, F. C., Lipman, L. N., and Woernley, D. L. (1960). Separation of univalent fragments from the bivalent rabbit antibody molecule by reduction of disulfide bonds. Arch. Biochem. Biophys. *89:* 230–244.

Nisonoff, A., and Woernley, D. L. (1959). Effect of hydrolysis by papain on the combining sites of an antibody. Nature *183:* 1325–1326.

Osserman, E. F., and Takatsuki, K. (1964). Clinical and immunochemical studies of four cases of heavy (H-γ2) chain disease. Am. J. Med. *37:* 351–373.

Ouchterlony, O. (1953). Antigen-antibody reactions in gels. IV. Types of reactions in co-ordinated system of diffusion. Acta Pathol. Microbiol. Scand. *32:* 231–240.

Oudin, J. (1956). Réaction de précipitation spécifique entre des sérums d'animaux de même espèce. Compt. Rend. *242:* 2489–2490.

Oudin, J. (1960). Allotypes of rabbit serum proteins. I. Immunochemical analysis leading to the individualization of seven main allotypes. J. Exptl. Med. *112:* 107–124.

Palmer, J. L., Mandy, W. J., and Nisonoff, A. (1962). Heterogeneity of rabbit antibody and its subunits. Proc. Natl. Acad. Sci. U. S. *48:* 49–53.

Palmer, J. L., and Nisonoff, A. (1964). Dissociation of rabbit γ-globulin into half-molecules after reduction of one labile disulfide bond. Biochemistry *3:* 863–869.

Palmer, J. L., Nisonoff, A., and Van Holde, K. E. (1963). Dissociation of rabbit gamma-globulin into subunits by reduction and acidification. Proc. Natl. Acad. Sci. U. S. *50:* 314–321.

Parfentjev, I. A. (1936). U. S. Patent 2065196.

Perlzweig, W. A., Delrue, G., and Geschickter, C. (1928). Hyperproteinemia associated with multiple myelomas. J. Am. Med. Assoc. *90:* 755–757.

Phelps, R. A., Neet, K. E., Lynn, L. T., and Putnam, F. W. (1961). The cupric ion catalysis of the cleavage of γ-globulin and other proteins by hydrogen peroxide. J. Biol. Chem. *236:* 96–105.

Pope, C. G. (1938). Disaggregation of proteins by enzymes. Brit. J. Exptl. Pathol. *19:* 245–251.

Pope, C. G. (1939). The action of proteolytic enzymes on the antitoxins and proteins in immune sera. I. True digestion of the proteins. Brit. J. Exptl. Pathol. *20:* 132–149.

Pope, C. G. (1939). The action of proteolytic enzymes on the antitoxins and proteins in immune sera. II. Heat denaturation after partial enzyme action. Brit. J. Exptl. Pathol. *20:* 201–212.

Porter, R. R. (1950). The formation of a specific inhibitor by hydrolysis of rabbit antiovalbumin. Biochem. J. *46:* 479–484.

Porter, R. R. (1958). Separation and isolation of fractions of rabbit gamma-globulin containing the antibody and antigenic combining sites. Nature *182:* 670–671.

Porter, R. R. (1959). The hydrolysis of rabbit γ-globulin and antibodies with crystalline papain. Biochem. J. *73:* 119–126.

Poulik, M. D., and Edelman, G. M. (1961). Comparison of reduced alkylated derivatives of some myeloma globulins and Bence-Jones proteins. Nature *191:* 1274–1276.

Putnam, F. W. (1953). N-Terminal groups of normal human gamma globulin and of myeloma proteins. J. Am. Chem. Soc. *75:* 2785–2786.

Putnam, F. W. (1962). Structural relationships among normal human γ-globulin, myeloma globulins, and Bence-Jones proteins. Biochim. Biophys. Acta *63:* 539–541.

Putnam, F. W., Easley, C. W., Lynn, L. T., Ritchie, A. E., and Phelps, R. A. (1959). The heat precipitation of Bence-Jones proteins. I. Optimum conditions. Arch. Biochem. Biophys. *83:* 115–130.

Putnam, F. W., and Stelos, P. (1953). Proteins in multiple myeloma. II. Bence-Jones proteins. J. Biol. Chem. *203:* 347–358.

Putnam, F. W., Tan, M., Lynn, L. T., Easley, C. W., and Migita, S. (1962). The cleavage of rabbit γ-globulin by papain. J. Biol. Chem. *237:* 717–726.

Ropartz, C., Lenoir, J., and Rivat, L. (1961). A new inheritable property of human sera: the InV factor. Nature *189:* 586.

Schwartz, J. H., and Edelman, G. M. (1963). Comparisons of Bence-Jones proteins and L polypeptide chains of myeloma globulins after hydrolysis with trypsin. J. Exptl. Med. *118:* 41–53.

Webb, T., Rose, B., and Sehon, A. H. (1958). Biocolloids in normal human urine. II. Physicochemical and immunochemical characteristics. Can. J. Biochem. Physiol. *36:* 1167–1175.

5

The Active Sites of Antibodies

1. The enzyme analogy

A routine procedure for investigating the binding-site topology of enzymes involves the identification of specific amino acid residues that participate in the reaction of enzyme with substrate, the determination of amino acid sequences in the various chains that make up the enzyme, and the location of the active amino acids in their proper positions in these chains. From such information patterns of substrate specificity can be constructed, the size of the active region can be determined, and the influence of tertiary protein structure upon the specificity of the primary structures can be inferred.

Since antibody interactions with antigens are in many ways similar to enzyme-substrate combinations, e.g., in the magnitude of the reaction patterns, one would naturally expect that this same routine procedure could be used for investigating the active sites of antibodies. Only limited success has been obtained, however, since heterogeneity extends right into the active-site patterns and makes amino acid analyses less meaningful than in the case of enzymes.

Before considering data pertaining to the active-site topology of antibodies, therefore, it should be instructive to examine the structure of an enzyme and to obtain thereby a few guides for interpreting antibody data. The enzymatic properties of α-chymotrypsin, as discussed by D. E. Koshland, Jr. (1963), depend upon at least three different amino acids—serine, methionine, and histidine—but these three do not form a sequential pattern in linear array. In fact, the active histidine is present on the B chain of the enzyme while the active methionine and serine are located on the C chain. In three-dimensional orientation the histidine, methionine, and serine are close to each other, when bound to substrate, with histidine and serine most intimately involved. Methionine can be photo-oxidized with loss of only two-thirds of enzyme activity whereas phosphorylation of serine or photo-oxidation of histidine results in complete loss. Koshland regards the active (surface) methionine, therefore, to reside at the periphery of the active site and, in spite of its nearness to serine (only three residues away), not to be completely involved in substrate binding.

At one time it was widely believed that an active-site pattern most certainly should involve a set sequence of amino acids in a given chain of an enzyme. This may still be true in certain cases but it cannot be assumed to be true in all cases. Interactivity of substrate with semi-sites at two or more different parts of an enzyme protein molecule, as in the case of α-chymotrypsin, can also occur. Through folding and coiling of a protein molecule these semi-sites are brought adjacent to each other to act as an "active patch" on the protein surface.

The question remains whether, for each type of enzyme (and, presumably, each type of antibody), the "active patch" is preformed in a somewhat rigid structure or whether the semi-sites are brought into proper orientation at the time of substrate interaction. In the case of phosphoglucomutase Koshland concluded that protein conformation took place at the time of substrate interaction and that the active site was flexible, i.e., that semi-sites were brought into juxtaposition as a result of binding to substrate. If an "active patch" is composed of semi-sites from different parts of a molecule and yet is more or less rigid and preformed, then tertiary structures (those involved in protein folding and coiling) must play a part in determining specificity. Such structures would determine the preformed orientation of the various parts of the "active patch."

Any substantial conformational rearrangement at the time of interaction, necessitated by flexibility of active-site substructures, would require additional activation energy and heat of reaction, and would result in lower specific rate reaction constants than those for preformed active-site patterns. In the case of antibodies reactive with dinitrophenyl (DNP) haptens, preformed active sites would appear to be indicated, for this particular antibody-hapten reaction exemplifies one of the fastest bimolecular reactions in homogeneous solution known to immunochemistry. With a rate constant approaching $1 \times 10^7 \ \text{M}^{-1} \ \text{sec}^{-1}$ and yet with a required activation energy of only 4 kcal/mole, any major conformational change during the reaction of anti-DNP with DNP would certainly be contraindicated (L. A. Day, Sturtevant, and Singer, 1963).

As will be discussed more thoroughly in Chapter 7, the measurement of the velocity of forward reactions between antibodies and their antigenic counterparts is difficult to obtain except in very special cases. Thus, it is not yet possible to generalize that all antigen-antibody reactions have such high rate constants as their limit or that all reactions require such minimal activation energies, and therefore to generalize that the active sites of all antibodies are preformed and presumably rigid. One can only say that this is true in some cases—in anti-DNP, for example, and also in anti-benzenearsonate (anti-Rp). In the latter case Froese, Sehon, and Eigen (1962) obtained a value of 2×10^7 M^{-1} sec^{-1} as the limiting rate constant, which again is extremely high. Even in these instances there is a display of heterogeneity in kinetic behavior which appears to be associated with heterogeneity among the active sites of individual molecules. This would open the possibility that some sites are preformed and rigid while others, in the same population, are fully formed only when antigen is present but otherwise flexible and disunited. Further investigations along these lines would have to be carried out before such a possibility could be shown to be true or false.

Three complications make such investigations difficult. The first is that most antibody-hapten reactions are measured by establishment of equilibrium conditions between the forward bimolecular reactions and a reverse monomolecular dissociation. In the first-order reverse dissociation of DNP-anti-DNP the rate constant is only 1 sec^{-1} while that of Rp-anti-Rp is 50 sec^{-1}. Thus, while the rate of combination in each system is nearly the same, the equilibrium constants of the two differ by two orders of magnitude. Heterogeneity of rate constants for a given system is best revealed by studying equilibrium conditions, but then it is not known whether such heterogeneity expresses a distribution among both forward and reverse rate constants or primarily in just one direction.

The second complication arises from the varied nature of antigens that combine with their respective antibodies. While many haptenic groups are relatively small, the reactive determinant groups of many known antigens are considerably larger with perhaps as many as six linked organic residues participating in the reaction with certain active antibody sites. Under such circumstances one could visualize a range of areas for the active patch of an antibody surface to accommodate a range of sizes of antigenic determinant groups. Preformed semi-sites may perhaps react effectively with small haptenic groups as though they were completed sites whereas conformation of full-sized active sites may have to take place, subsequent to semi-site reaction, before antibodies can bind effectively with larger complex determinant groups.

The third complication has less to do with antibody than with antigen. It involves the rate of diffusion of antibody and antigen toward each other. If every collision of reactants resulted in immediate union then the rate of diffusion would be the rate-limiting step. For small uncharged haptens with spherical symmetry, diffusion would limit the rate constant to 10^9 M^{-1} sec^{-1} and would require an energy (apparent activation energy) of 4–5 kcal/mole to overcome solvent viscosity (L. A. Day et al., 1963). Since the reactions of anti-DNP and of anti-Rp with their respective haptens approached but did not reach this limit, one presumes that diffusion was not rate-limiting in these instances. Talmage and Cann (1961) have suggested that since the Q_{10} for certain antigen-antibody reactions is 1.4 and since the Q_{10} for diffusion processes is also about 1.4, such reactions may be diffusion-controlled. Q_{10}, of course, is the increase in rate of reactant association as temperature is increased in increments of 10°C from 0 to 40°C.

2. Asymmetrical placement of the active antibody site

It has already been indicated in the last chapter that limited enzymatic degradation of an immunoglobulin can occur without loss of binding-site activity. Fragmentation studies revealed that the binding sites of rabbit IgG were asymmetrically placed on the molecule, that pepsin would cleave the molecule to form a fragment with two combining sites still intact, and that reduction of the bivalent fragment would form two active univalent fragments with site topology virtually intact.

Earlier work had already indicated that the active sites of a horse-antitoxin antibody were only a small fraction of the total protein molecule and that they were asymmetrically placed. The problem that prevented generalization at this earlier date stemmed from the use of horse antitoxin against diphtheria as the antibody source. In many ways this horse immunoglobulin (now thought to be a horse IgA) had reaction characteristics, particularly in the precipitin reaction, that set it apart from the more usual antibody reactants. For example, it would form flocculents with toxin rather than true precipitins (cf. Chapter 8). Since it was a pseudoglobulin rather than a euglobulin there was additional question as to whether it should be included in the category of general antibody reactants at all. The reason for intensive interest in the antitoxin was its clinical rôle in diphtheria control, and it had been hoped that enzymatic fragmentation would result in an antitoxin with full retention of potency but with less horse globulin antigenicity when injected into humans. As discussed in the previous chapter the Parfentjev and the Pope processes accomplished this goal.

Pappenheimer and his colleagues investigated the properties of the horse antitoxin in depth. Partial digestion of antitoxin with pepsin according to the Parfentjev process resulted in nearly twice as many units of specific antibody nitrogen per milligram of toxin-antitoxin precipitate as undigested antitoxin (Pappenheimer and Robinson, 1937). Utilizing the Langmuir-Schaeffer method of monomolecular adsorption of substances on stearate films, Porter and Pappenheimer (1939) showed that when diphtheria toxin was adsorbed first, giving a thickness of 33 Å, a layer of antitoxin with a thickness of 49 ± 2 Å would adsorb to the toxin layer. However, the antitoxin layer would not adsorb toxin to form a third layer even though it would adsorb toxin if layered first on the stearate film. This was contrary to their experience with pneumococcal polysaccharides (Ps) and horse anti-Ps antibodies (IgM) in which reactions took place regardless of layering order and multiple layers of antigens and antibodies could be formed.

From this evidence it was concluded "that the antitoxic groups are distributed in an unsymmetrical manner on the antitoxin molecule and that a large inactive portion of the molecule is split off by treatment with the enzymes," and, further, "that the antitoxic groups may lie fairly close together on one side only of the antitoxin molecule, in contrast to other precipitating antibodies, and therefore the formation of a lattice leading to precipitation is impossible, from steric considerations, in regions of antitoxin excess where toxin molecules are saturated with antitoxin" (Pappenheimer, Lundgren, and Williams, 1940).

The placement of the active sites of horse anti-diphtheria toxin can thus be visualized as similar to those of rabbit IgG. The problem now is that since rabbit antibodies form precipitins with antigens in the classical manner to be discussed later and since they are similar to horse antitoxins with respect to active-site placement, the argument that Pappenheimer *et al.* (1940) used to explain the unusual precipitation characteristics of toxin-antitoxin is lost. Better explanations are needed for the lack of adsorption of toxin to a monolayer of antitoxin as the antibody is spread on the barium stearate film as well as for the flocculation reactions. These might be sought in some other characteristic of horse IgA.[1]

3. The lower limit of the size of antibody sites

One of the classical experiments in immunochemistry that still enters into lively discussions concerning antibody structure is that of Landsteiner and van der Scheer (1938). Contained therein are data related to antigenic specificity, to antibody heterogeneity, and to the effective lower limit of the size of antibody sites. Landsteiner and van der Scheer prepared the complex hapten, *sym*-aminoisophthalylglycineleucine (GIL), in which the two amino acids extended outwards in opposite directions from the central aminophenyl group:

---

[1] Physical properties (Pappenheimer, Lundgren, and Williams, 1940): $s_{20} = 7.2 \times 10^{-13}$ cm sec^{-1} dyne^{-1}; $D = 4.40 \times 10^{-7}$ cm^2 sec^{-1}; $\mu = 2.6 \times 10^{-5}$ cm^2 volt^{-1} sec^{-1}; $\bar{V} = 0.736$; $f/f_0 = 1.4$; nitrogen content $= 14.3\%$; galactose-mannose-glucosamine content $= 2.5\%$.

$$NH_2$$

$$HOOC-CH_2-NH-CO- \underset{}{\bigcirc} -CO-NH-\underset{CH_2-CH(CH_3)_2}{\overset{COOH}{\underset{|}{CH}}}$$

GIL

By attaching the hapten to the washed stromata of horse red blood cells through a diazo link to the central phenyl group of the hapten, and by immunizing rabbits with the azostromata, antisera were obtained that would precipitate the hapten diazotized to otherwise non-reactive chicken serum protein.

Two other azostromata were also prepared, one with m-aminobenzoylglycine (G) and the other with m-aminobenzoylleucine (L), to be used as insoluble absorbents for removing antibodies from the test antisera. G and L were also diazotized to chicken serum protein to be used as precipitating antigens in the same way as GIL-serum.

$$NH_2 \qquad\qquad NH_2$$

$$HOOC-CH_2-NH-CO-\bigcirc \qquad \bigcirc-CO-NH-\underset{CH_2-CH(CH_3)_2}{\overset{COOH}{\underset{|}{CH}}}$$

G   L

It can be seen in Table 8 that absorption with G-azostromata removed antibodies that would precipitate with G-azoprotein but left antibodies that would precipitate with L-azoprotein; likewise, that absorption with L-azostromata removed antibodies that would precipitate with L-azoprotein but left antibodies that would precipitate with G-azoprotein. Absorption with a mixture of G- and L-azostromata removed both types of precipitating antibodies simultaneously. Absorptions with either azostromata alone, moreover, did not affect antibody precipitation with GIL-azoprotein. Only when absorption with combined G- and L-azostromata was carried out did the antiserum show nearly complete loss of precipitating power with GIL-azoprotein.

Landsteiner and van der Scheer concluded that these experiments as well as similar ones with succinic and phenylarsenic acid residues "definitely establish the existence of cases in which discrete antibodies are formed that are individually directed towards separate determinant groups in one substance, even though it be of small molecular size and the determinant groups rather closely adjoining." The authors com-

TABLE 8

*Effects of Absorption of Rabbit Anti-GIL-Azostromata (Horse) with G- and
L-Azostromata upon Precipitation with GIL-, G-, and L-Azoproteins*

Absorbing Azostromata (Horse)	Test Azoprotein (chicken)	Unabsorbed*	Absorbed Once	Absorbed Twice	Absorbed Three Times
G	GIL	+++±	+++±	+++±	+++±
	G	+	0	0	0
	L	++±	++±	++±	++±
L	GIL	+++±	++±	++	++
	G	+	+	+	+
	L	++±†	0	0	0
G + L	GIL	+++±	+±	±	*tr*
	G	+	0	0	0
	L	++±	tr	0	0

(Constructed from Landsteiner and van der Scheer, 1938.)

* Intensity of reactions were graded: 0, faint trace, trace (tr), *trace* (*tr*), +,
±, +, +±, ++, ++±, +++, +++±, ++++. Overnight readings only are
given above although 1-hour readings were also given in the original paper.

† This value appeared as "0" in the original paper and was also reproduced as
such in Landsteiner's book, Table 36. It obviously was a typographical error in
the original article that was carried over uncorrected in the book. A zero reading
would mean that no antibody had reacted with L from the unabsorbed serum,
which, of course, would have made the whole paper and discussion pointless.
The authors state in the text that "the separation of two sorts of antibodies in
GIL serum by absorption is demonstrated . . ., there being stronger reactions
on the leucine than on the glycine moiety."

mented further upon the results and contrasted them with data obtained
with "multiple" antibodies (Landsteiner and van der Scheer, 1936):

> The failure of repeated absorption with an antigen which contains
> only one of the two groupings, to effect a significant diminution of
> the antibody reacting with the other group, is proof for the serologi-
> cal kinship between the two antibodies demonstrated. It is in con-
> trast to the behavior of multiple but related antibodies developed
> through the stimulus of a single determinant structure, where con-
> tinued absorption with a reacting heterologous antigen was often
> seen to exhaust the immune serum completely.

Campbell and Bulman (1954) calculated the area of an active patch
on an anti-GIL antibody surface that would be most complementary to
the two classes of GIL determinant groups and obtained a value of 700
Å². What made the situation confusing was their suggestion that this

might fix the upper limit of the combining site. That it did so for anti-GIL antibodies in the sera that Landsteiner and van der Scheer used is unquestionable. Other discussants, however, tried to generalize that perhaps this was the upper limit of all antibodies and that heterogeneity within a population of antibodies for various adjacent groupings on an antigen would explain seemingly larger combining sites.

Levine (1963), however, demonstrated larger combining sites in rabbit antibody to benzylpenicilloyl (BPO) groups in a Landsteiner-van der Scheer type of experiment. The BPO groups have a phenylacetylamine side and a thiazolidinecarboxylic acid side symmetrical to a midway carboxyl group. The carboxyl reacts with the ϵ-amino groups of lysine in polylysine to produce a haptenic structure quite similar in size and shape to GIL-azostromata.

BPO-lysine

The question was raised whether rabbit antisera would form only to the phenylacetylamine end or to the thiazolidinecarboxylic acid end or perhaps form against intermediate portions thereof. The results quite conclusively showed, even after considerations of heterogeneity had been made, that the pool of six rabbit sera against BPO-rabbit normal serum and tested with BPO-polylysine contained no antibodies against end structures but rather had antibodies encompassing the entire BPO group, lysine side chain, and even adjacent peptides of the carrier protein. It was clear that the active patch of antibody surface in this instance was much greater than 700 Å^2. Isliker (1962), on the other hand, calculated on the basis of serologically active fragments that an active surface patch need be only 100–200 Å^2. Assuming a total surface area of 26,000 Å^2, the active site would in this case represent only 0.4–0.7 % of the total protein surface.

As will be made clearer later on, antibody activity can be inhibited by substances that bind with much less than the total active site. Thus, the fact that an antibody binds with a small grouping does not delineate the site as being necessarily small. The GIL type of experiment is therefore important in that it presents a potential haptenic grouping slightly larger than can ordinarily accommodate antibody. One has little control over production of antibodies with active sites of a certain size, and one can only take the smallest upper limit described for individual antibody preparations (such as Isliker's 100–200 Å²) as descriptive of the smallest total area that can be attained. Kabat (1961) has emphasized this point—that while available data can establish an upper limit for the complementary area of the antibody combining site, they "provide no insight into how small an antibody cavity can be." Can an antibody site be totally directed, for example, against a determinant as small as a single glucose residue? At the *Gatlinburg Symposium on Antibodies* Kabat (1957) treated the Landsteiner-van der Scheer GIL experiment in much the same way as he did in 1961, but was unable, apparently, to focus the attention of all in attendance upon this crucial point. Pressman (1957), for example, in the published discussion following Kabat's paper stated:

> I would like to correct Dr. Kabat's statement about Dr. Landsteiner's study because I have used this same example but I have always used it differently—I think the way Landsteiner used it!

Pressman was emphasizing the heterogeneity of antibody formation against complex haptens and, after describing the GIL experiment, concluded:

> This shows that antibodies formed against the single substance were heterogeneous because they could get antibodies with two different specificities. They also found a *sizable portion* of the antibody that would react only with antigen containing the homologous hapten group, and here they had antibody that required both the leucyl and glycyl groups, which I presume you would say would be the measure of the size of the grouping. [*Italics mine.*]

Kabat, not wishing his own point to be lost, merely replied that as he remembered it *not too much was obtained* here. Landsteiner and van der Scheer (1938), in discussing this particular aspect, had stated: "There were *practically no antibodies* in the sera examined which were not removable by absorption with both 'partial' antigens." Table 8 shows that a *strong trace* of antibody, not removable by three repeated absorptions, did remain in the antiserum that would precipitate GIL-azoprotein. This was hardly a *sizable portion*, but did persist enough to indicate a certain amount of heterogeneity. Nevertheless, in spite of this non sequitur to Kabat's argument that prevented the argument from being clearly made, *it was evident that by far the greatest amount of antibody did not have sites complementary to the two determinants as a whole.*

Kreiter and Pressman (1964) reopened the question of heterogeneity among anti-GIL antibodies once more in experiments designed to separate the various antibody species—anti-G, anti-L, and anti-GIL—and to test their cross-reactivity with G, L, and/or GIL. They concluded that although a major part of the binding energy of hapten and antibody was supplied by either leucine or glycine, the remaining amino acid did contribute to the binding energy to a certain extent. Their view, therefore, was that the combining site was directed against a large part of the immunizing hapten. The conclusions depended on an assumption of considerable purity of the various antibody species (and such resolution is extremely difficult to obtain!) but accepting for the moment that high resolution had been obtained and that the conclusions were valid, the point is that such conclusions would be valid only for the Kreiter-Pressman sera and not necessarily for the Landsteiner-van der Scheer sera. Because of heterogeneity in reactivity from one serum to the next, it is impossible to prove or disprove a point made with one serum by testing the reaction with another.

We have as yet no way of producing antibodies in animals with uniform sizes of antibody sites and no way of measuring such uniformity if it were obtained. All we can measure at the present time is the rough upper limit obtained in individual cases. The existence of heterogeneity merely serves to make the problem even more complex and exceedingly more difficult to resolve. We can only accept Isliker's 100–200 Å^2 as the smallest complete active site so far obtained.

4. The upper limit of the size of antibody sites

Landsteiner and van der Scheer (1932, 1934), in their initial investigations on the serological specificity of peptides, had concluded that terminal amino acids played a major rôle in the specificity of small peptide chains. When, in a later report (1939), they extended their experimentation to larger synthetic peptide units, they revised their notion for they noted that strong reactions involved not only end groups but other parts of the molecule as well. The following pentapeptides were prepared:

Tetraglycylglycine	G_5
Tetraglycylleucine	G_4L
d,l-Diglycylleucylglycylglycine	G_2LG_2
Trileucylglycylglycine	L_3G_2

The pentapeptides were coupled to horse azostromata for use in immunizing rabbits and for absorption, and were coupled to chicken serum protein for use as test antigens in the precipitin reaction. Regardless of whether carboxyl or amino groups were prominent, antibodies appeared to be specific for an entire pentapeptide and not just a portion thereof. Moreover, a disparity in the reaction of antibody with peptides as compared with the corresponding amides revealed a difference between acid and other polar groups in their conferral of specificity. The authors suggested that specific combinations occurring in antigen-antibody reactions were not all of the same kind, i.e., that antibody sites did not always contain the same limited number of elements merely arranged in different ways. And they pointed out that perhaps their pentapeptides were not of sufficient size to reach the uppermost possible limit of antibody-site conformation.

Sage, Deutsch, Fasman, and Levine (1964) found that in the poly-alanine system the most inhibitory hapten was also the pentamer, and that the six-membered chain of alanine residues was actually less effective. It was noted that beginning with the hexamer there was an increasing tendency towards α-helical formation, but perhaps not enough to account for the three-fold difference in the inhibiting efficiencies between the pentamer and the hexamer. The size of the penta-L-alanine molecule in extended form was calculated to be 25 Å × 11 Å × 6.5 Å, for which an antibody combining site in the form of Karush's (1956) interhelical cavity, which would encompass the hapten, would present an over-all surface somewhere in the neighborhood of 2000 Å². The size was found to be little different from Kabat's isomaltohexaose, to be discussed below.

To go much beyond the pentapeptide size of chain length may not be too instructive in determining the corresponding size of antibody sites since, as Maurer (1963) points out:

> ... when we talk of the amino acid residues constituting an antigenic site, we may not be referring to a sequence of amino acids in a protein chain in a chemical sense, but to the residues which are physically adjacent to each other in the coiled three-dimensional protein structure, that is a patch on the protein surface. In other words, if the same globular proteins were to be extended, the adjacent amino acid residues of the reactive site might in fact be separated by several amino acid residues.

In essence when an active patch on an antibody protein surface reacts with an active patch on an antigenic protein surface, each patch may be composed of semi-sites from different parts of each protein molecule which are so oriented as to provide a continuum of activity. Measurements of surface area in such instances would require techniques and instrumentation that would stretch even the best immunochemist's imagination and know-how.

The experiments of Kabat (1954, 1956, 1960) have approached the problem from a different direction and have provided a little less ambiguity in interpretation. Kabat and Berg (1952, 1953) had shown that dextrans—simple polymers of glucose joined mainly by the α $(1 \rightarrow 6)$ link—were antigenic in man, and this prompted Kabat to raise two questions: Was the antibody specific for the α $(1 \rightarrow 6)$ linked anhydroglucopyranose units? How many linked glucose residues were necessary to fill the antibody combining site completely? He first found that the antibodies did not react well with members of the α $(1 \rightarrow 4)$-linked series such as maltose or with those of the β $(1 \rightarrow 6)$-linked polymers such as gentiobiose. Only those of the α $(1 \rightarrow 6)$ series—isomaltose, isomaltotriose, etc.—reacted well.

In his 1954 paper Kabat reported that three times the amount of 4-α-isomaltotriose-D-glucose was needed to inhibit antidextran activity as the parent compound, isomaltotriose. Since the derivative was α $(1 \rightarrow 6)$-linked in the first three residues, in the same manner as the parent, but had an additional glucose unit linked α $(1 \rightarrow 4)$, Kabat predicted that the antibody site should accommodate more than three α $(1 \rightarrow 6)$-linked residues, i.e., isomaltotetraose. Two years later when the tetraose, pentaose, and hexaose were made available, the prediction was confirmed. The tetraose fitted better than the triose, the pentaose had even better inhibitory power, and the hexaose, with only slightly better inhibition, appeared to establish the upper limit. Because of heterogeneity there was the possibility that a heptasaccharide might on occasion be superior.

As shown in Figure 17 the model of isomaltohexaose would be free to rotate about the α $(1 \rightarrow 6)$ links and to form a number of shapes in a random coil from a compact molecule to a fully extended one. Heterogeneity would therefore be extensive but with preservation of complementarity to the α $(1 \rightarrow 6)$ linkages. In the fully extended form, dimensions of the hexasaccharide would be 34 Å $\times$ 12 Å $\times$ 7 Å, and an antibody combining site in the form of Karush's (1956) interhelical cavity that would encompass the hapten would present an over-all surface somewhere in the neighborhood of 2000 Å². Whether the extended form would actually exist in vivo in an antibody-producing host is an open question, but the hypothetical site surface formed around it would be maximal and still a relatively small part of the total immunoglobulin surface.

Sage et al. (1964) questioned whether such a deep and large-surfaced interhelical cavity at an antibody site actually would exist. They based their reservation upon the fact that binding of the penta-L-alanine

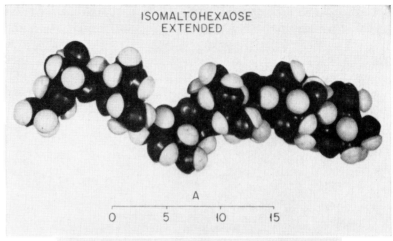

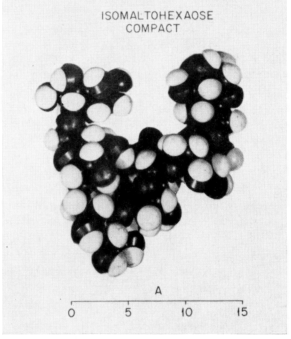

FIG. 17. Extended and compact models of isomaltohexaose. (Kabat, 1957.)

depended much more upon the maintenance of an uninterrupted sequence, regardless of position, than upon a terminal status, obviously necessary for deep-cavity binding. A shallow antibody-site cavity appeared much more likely with a size, as one can easily calculate, not much more than 700 Å^2. Mage and Kabat (1963), themselves, considered the ramifications of the shallow-cavity hypothesis of an antibody site. In such a case it would be possible to visualize a site size much smaller than the size of the most effective hapten. The oversized hapten either would have a statistically larger number of ways of fitting the site than a small hapten or would much more easily fold to a specific conformation representative of the specific site surface. The former alternative would best fit the data of Landsteiner and van der Scheer and of Sage *et al.* (1964), where folded conformation of short polypeptides was unlikely. Either alternative would fit Kabat's dextran data and also those of Stollar, Levine, Lehrer, and Van Vunakis (1962), in which the upper limit of inhibiting power of the polynucleotides of thymine for anti-deoxyribonucleic acid (DNA) was the pentathymidylic acid.

The assumption of a shallow binding site for the pentapeptides, the hexasaccharides, and the pentanucleotides would actually offer substantial agreement with Karush's so-called deep site against a relatively small hapten as well as with Beiser and Tanenbaum's (1963) calculation of a binding-site size for antibody against the hapten, β-D-galactoside. But such an assumption, the most likely one that one can at present make, would also make the establishment of the upper limit of an antibody binding-site surface area as indeterminable as the establishment of the lower limit. Kabat's words (1957) indeed form a fitting conclusion to this section: "It is obvious that an increased knowledge of the dimensions, architecture, and heterogeneity of antibody-combining sites will play an important rôle in our understanding of the relations between immunological specificity and chemical structure."

5. The chemical nature of combining sites

Returning for the moment to the enzyme model, chymotrypsin, which was discussed at the beginning of this chapter, one will recall that the histidine residue on the B chain was found to be active in the enzyme site. Photo-oxidation of histidine had resulted in enzyme activity loss, but, as D. E. Koshland, Jr. (1963), pointed out, this effect in itself did not establish histidine as a part of the active site. Its position might have been a distant point where its presence might have been necessary to maintain tertiary structure. Modification there might have resulted in protein unfolding and loss of support for the active site. The experi-

ments of Schoellman and Shaw (1962), however, established the direct
rôle of histidine in the enzyme site. By choosing a substrate that was also
an alkylating agent, specific alkylation of amino acids at the enzyme
site where substrate was bound could be subsequently carried out.
Alkylated histidine was recovered when the reaction mixture was analyzed.

In the same year and in the same general way Wofsy, Metzger, and
Singer labeled the active site of an antihapten antibody preparation.
The antibody was prepared against p-azobenzenearsonate (Rpz) and was
reacted with p-(arsonic acid)-benzenediazonium fluoborate (Rpz-FB);
the Rpz-FB was preferentially guided to the active site by virtue of its
haptenic specificity; side chains in the active site were then made to
react with the functional diazonium group; and tyrosine was found to be
the principal amino acid at the site that was labeled. The technique was
also successfully applied to the 2,4-dinitrophenyllysine system. The
method, called *affinity labeling*, should prove generally useful in un-
covering other site-specific amino acids.

Tyrosine had previously been implicated in the active sites of various
antibodies but not with such convincing evidence as presented by the
affinity-labeling experiments. Pressman and Roholt (1961), for example,
attempted to label exposed tyrosine in an Fab-fragment except those at
the active site, which were protected by adsorbed hapten. In essence
this would seemingly have provided a mirror image to affinity labeling.
Papain-fragmented rabbit anti-p-azobenzoate (anti-Xpz) was purified
for Fab-fragment, mixed with p-aminobenzoate (Xpa), and iodinated
with 6–7 atoms of carrier containing ^{131}I, the iodine reacting mainly with
tyrosine residues. Another portion, not protected with Xpa, was iodinated with a similar amount of carrier containing ^{125}I. The two labeled
preparations were then freed of unbound iodide and hapten, digested in
formic acid with pepsin, and subjected to two-dimensional paper electrophoresis and chromatography to separate the various peptides. Two
peptide regions contained relatively more ^{125}I than ^{131}I, compared to the
total, while one region contained less. The remaining regions (about
75% of the total) contained equivalent amounts of each. It was suggested
at the time that the unbalanced regions represented tyrosine-containing
peptides derived from the active site.

But, as D. E. Koshland, Jr. (1963), pointed out at the 1962 conference
on *Antibody To Enzymes*, the classical interpretation of a "protection"
experiment remains in doubt:

> A residue labeled in the absence of hapten and not labeled in the
> presence of hapten is conventionally presumed to be at the active

site. It is possible however that the protection occurs because of a refolding of the molecule and the labeled group is actually a group made less reactive by refolding at some distant position of the tertiary structure.

Indeed, Roholt, Radzimski, and Pressman (1963) found that when they repeated their experiments (except this time also to separate the light and heavy chains prior to final digestion for peptides) the peptides with unbalanced ratios of the two isotopes were contained wholly in the light chains!

The bulk of present evidence points to the heavy chains rather than the light chains as the main center for the active site. Fleischman, Pain, and Porter (1962) obtained the first substantial indication that the heavy chains, when separated by mild reduction from the light chains, carried with them a large share of the binding activity for protein. Metzger and Singer (1963), using a rabbit antibody to dinitrophenyl-lysine, found that when the antibody was mildly reduced in the presence of hapten and separated into heavy and light chains, the hapten-binding capacity was again wholly associated with heavy chains. In this case, however, some of the light chains remained with the heavy chain-hapten fraction, reducing the yield of free light chains by one-third. No hapten was associated with light chains alone.

Utsumi and Karush (1964) prepared from purified antihapten antibody a mildly reduced and alkylated rabbit IgG that retained its antihapten activity, and then separated it carefully into its subunits by molecular-sieve filtration in the presence of a neutral and dilute detergent. Immunological activity was present in the heavy chains as revealed by binding of the homologous hapten during equilibrium dialysis. Negative energy of binding was 8.28 kcal/mole, a loss of only 13 % from that of original reduced and alkylated antibody. The authors concluded tentatively:

> ... that the antibody-combining region is exclusively associated with the A [heavy] chain and that the stated difference [13% loss] was probably due to aggregation and/or denaturation of the A chain. It is suggested that the B [light] chain serves to prevent these effects and thereby indirectly contributes to the immunologic reactivity. The apparent partial specificity of the B chain in enhancing the activity of the isolated A chain, reported by others, is attributed to a selection among the varieties of B chain of those which are most appropriate for complex formation with that portion of the A chain whose conformation is associated with its specific reactivity.

The partial specificity of the light chains (B chains in the quotation) referred to by Utsumi and Karush is exemplified by the work of Edelman, Benacerraf, and Ovary (1963). Antibodies were prepared in guinea pigs against a number of antigens and were then purified by dissociation from specific precipitates, reduced, alkylated, and separated by zone electrophoresis in 8 M urea at pH 3.5. A distinctive pattern of light chains was obtained for each type of antigen and confirmed their previous view that light-chain patterns (referred to by the authors according to an older nomenclature as L-chain patterns, L for *light*) of guinea pig antibodies of widely different specificities were different. These differences persisted from animal to animal and were therefore not due to variations among the guinea pigs themselves.

To bring the problem around full circle, Metzger, Wofsy, and Singer (1964) applied the technique of affinity labeling to the question of active-site participation by heavy vs. light chains. They found specifically labeled tyrosines, representative of the combining site, in both types of chains. It would appear that the total active patch of an antibody surface might easily be composed of semi-sites from two different chains, as in the case of chymotrypsin, but with the major binding energy contribution stemming from the heavy-chain semi-site pattern. The question to which Utsumi and Karush actually addressed themselves is outside the scope of this text: Is the specificity pattern of an active site created in an antibody-producing animal by production of the heavy chain alone, perhaps formed before linkage to a light chain, or is the specificity pattern created as a dual property of both chains? They are inclined to believe the former. But regardless of which answer is correct there is little question that in a fully formed active site, binding properties depend to a certain extent upon the nature of the light-chain moiety. Indeed, as shown by Hong and Nisonoff (1966), extent of binding depends upon a proper combination of light and heavy chains. From a single rabbit they isolated and separated from each other both low- and high-affinity antibodies to a single hapten. The fractions were further reduced and separated into light and heavy chains so that recombinations of light chains from low-affinity antibody could be made with heavy chains from high-affinity antibody and *vice versa*. Homologous recombinations and recombinations with chains from normal IgG served as controls. The results showed that light chains derived from high-affinity antibody were more effective than light chains from low-affinity antibody in restoring high-affinity complementation. Heterogeneity in light chain complementation was thus indicated and suggested that different clones of cells utilized different pairs of polypeptide chains in the synthesis of an antibody with a given binding affinity.

TABLE 9

Amino Acid Analysis of Two Purified Antibodies Isolated from the Same Rabbit

Amino Acid	Anti-Rpz	Anti-Apz
	*residues/molecule**	
Arginine.	44.7	42.5
Isoleucine.	48.4	46.4
Aspartic acid.	106	110
Glutamic acid.	125	127
Leucine.	89	91
Alanine.	81.1	81.4
Glycine.	110	110
Histidine.	16.4	16.6
Lysine.	69.6	69.4
Methionine.	13.8	13.5
Phenylalanine.	44.3	44.9
Proline.	109	110
Serine.	151	151
Threonine.	162	162
Tyrosine.	56.1	56.2
Valine.	128	128

(Reported by Koshland and Englberger, 1963.)

* Taken as 160.000 molecular weight.

There must, of course, be other amino acids besides tyrosine that participate in the specificity pattern of an active site. Affinity labeling of these other residues would offer the best direct evidence. In the absence of such data at the time of this writing there is only indirect information as to the possible nature of some of these. M. E. Koshland and Englberger (1963) have provided a most exacting amino acid analysis of two different purified antihapten-antibody fractions obtained from the same rabbit. One hapten was the negatively charged phenylarsonate ion (R) and the other was the positively charged phenyltrimethylammonium ion (A), both of which as the *p*-azo derivatives (Rpz and Apz) were used to immunize the same rabbit. The analyses (Table 9) revealed that the anti-Rpz antibody contained two more residues each of arginine and isoleucine than did the anti-Apz antibody whereas the anti-Apz antibody contained two more residues each of leucine and glutamic acid and four more of aspartic acid. The other amino acids, including tyrosine, were remarkably similar in the two antibody preparations. In view of our previous discussion it would be presumptuous to ascribe such differences to the active-site regions of the two antibodies. On the other hand, it would not be correct to consider the data meaningless. As a matter of fact, far more value can be derived from the principle of Koshland and Englberger's experiment than from the data analysis. The principle is this: Because of heterogeneity of antibody formation and possible variations in active-site structure from one animal to the next it would not be as revealing to perform analyses upon pooled immunoglobulins from a large number of animals as it would be to perform comparative analyses of different purified globulins from the same animal. To extract the maximum amount of information, comparative analyses of a number of individual immunoglobulins, specifically purified for antibody, should be performed, and should be made at the level of immunoglobulin fragments.

Gitlin and Merler (1961) did obtain suggestive data from the comparative analyses of peptides obtained from pooled rabbit antibodies to a number of specific pneumococcal polysaccharides. Each lot of antiserum to a given polysaccharide antigen was obtained from a pool of 2000–6000 hyperimmunized rabbits, and peptide analysis revealed possible small differences in both primary and tertiary structures between antibodies to any two of five different type-specific antigens. Analyses of papain-released fragments that were separated before subsequent digestion with subtilisin, chymotrypsin, or trypsin aided in the finding of differences. The investigators pointed out that not only allotypic differences (which might have been prominent in small pools of 5–50 rabbit globulins) were thus submerged, but also specific differences between antibodies to a given antigen.

The best choice of antibody for detailed studies on site structure would appear to be from one of three sources: large pools of serum from thousands of non-inbred rabbits as used by Gitlin and Merler, small pools of serum from 5–50 inbred rabbits, or serum from individual rabbits as exemplified by the work of Koshland and Englberger. The use of small pools of serum from non-inbred rabbits would present too many problems to make the study of subtle differences between different antibodies less than equivocal. With the average laboratory not equipped to handle thousands of rabbits, and with inbred rabbits not as yet commercially available in adequate numbers, there is really no choice for most investigators but to carry out studies on individual immunoglobulins in the manner of Koshland and Englberger, and to compile charts of individual analyses to find out wherein site structures have a common basis for a given antigen, wherein they differ from antigen to antigen, and wherein they display heterogeneity to each given antigen. To delineate the nature of site structures still further, the program clearly should be extended to several species of animals and to genetic variants within each species. Final compilation and analysis should clearly show the chemical nature of the active antibody sites.

Cognizant that their anti-Apz and anti-Rpz amino acid analyses were only suggestive, M. E. Koshland, Englberger, and Gaddone (1965) carried out extensive iodination studies and found that iodine-sensitive sites were not needed at all for anti-Apz activity, even in tertiary structures, even though they were necessary to retain full activity of anti-Rpz.[2]

REFERENCES

Beiser, S. M., AND Tanenbaum, S. W. (1963). Binding site topology of enzymes and antibodies induced by the same determinants. Ann. N. Y. Acad. Sci., *103:* 595–609.

Campbell, D. H., and Bulman, N. (1954). Some current concepts of the chemical nature of antigens and antibodies. Fortschr. Chem. Org. Naturstoffe *9:* 443–484.

Day, L. A., Sturtevant, J. M., and Singer, S. J. (1963). The kinetics of the reactions between antibodies to the 2,4-dinitrophenyl group and specific haptens. Ann. N. Y. Acad. Sci. *103:* 611–625.

Edelman, G. M., Benacerraf, B., and Ovary, Z. (1963). Structure and specificity of guinea pig 7S antibodies. J. Exptl. Med. *118:* 229–244.

Fleischman, J. B., Pain, R., and Porter, R. R. (1962). Reduction of γ-globulins. Arch. Biochem. Biophys. Suppl. 1, 174–180.

Froese, A., Sehon, A. H., and Eigen, M. (1962). Kinetic studies of protein-dye and antibody-hapten interactions with the temperature-jump method. Can. J. Chem. *40:* 1786–1797.

Gitlin, D., and Merler, E. (1961). A comparison of the peptides released from related rabbit antibodies by enzymatic hydrolysis. J. Exptl. Med. *114:* 217–230.

Hong, R., and Nisonoff, A. (1966). Heterogeneity in the complementation of polypeptide subunits of a purified antibody isolated from an individual rabbit. J. Immunol. *96:* 622–628.

Isliker, H. (1962). Chemical structure of antibodies. Gazz. Chim. Ital. *92:* 850–858.

Kabat, E. A. (1954). Some configurational requirements and dimensions of the combining site on an antibody to naturally occurring antigen. J. Am. Chem. Soc. *76:* 3709–3713.

Kabat, E. A. (1956). Heterogeneity in extent of the combining regions of human antidextran. J. Immunol. *77:* 377–385.

Kabat, E. A. (1957). Size and heterogeneity of the combining sites on an antibody molecule. J. Cellular Comp. Physiol. *50:* Suppl. 1, 97.

Kabat, E. A. (1960). The upper limit for the site of the human antidextran combining site. J. Immunol. *84:* 82–85.

Kabat, E. A. (1961). *Kabat and Mayer's Experimental Immunochemistry*, 2nd Ed., Charles C Thomas (Springfield, Ill., 905 pp.) p. 250.

Kabat, E. A. and Berg, D. (1952). Production of precipitins and cutaneous sensitivity in man by injection of small amounts of dextran. Ann. N. Y. Acad. Sci. *55:* 471–476.

---

[2] More will be said about this experiment in Chapter 10.

Kabat, E. A., and Berg, D. (1953). Dextran—an antigen in man. J. Immunol 70: 514–532.

Karush, F. (1956). The interaction of purified antibody with optically isomeric haptens. J. Am. Chem. Soc. 78: 5519–5526.

Koshland, D. E., Jr. (1963). Properties of the active site of enzymes. Ann. N. Y. Acad. Sci. 103: 630–642.

Koshland, M. E., and Englberger, F. (1963). Differences in the amino acid composition of two purified antibodies from the same rabbit. Proc. Natl. Acad. Sci. U. S. 50: 61–68.

Koshland, M. E., Englberger, F., and Gaddone, S. (1965). Evidence against the universality of a tyrosyl residue at antibody combining sites. Immunochemistry 2: 115–125.

Kreiter, V. P., and Pressman, D. (1964). Antibodies to a hapten with two determinant groups. Immunochemistry 1: 151–163.

Landsteiner, K., and van der Scheer, J., (1932). On the serological specificity of peptides. J. Exptl. Med. 55: 781–796.

Landsteiner, K., and van der Scheer, J. (1934). On the serological specificity of peptides. J. Exptl. Med. 59: 769–780.

Landsteiner, K., and van der Scheer, J. (1936). On cross reactions of immune sera to azoproteins. J. Exptl. Med. 63: 325–339.

Landsteiner, K., and van der Scheer, J. (1938). On cross reactions of immune sera to azoproteins. II. Antigens with azocomponents containing two determinant groups. J. Exptl. Med. 67: 709–723.

Landsteiner, K., and van der Scheer, J. (1939). On the serological specificity of peptides. J. Exptl. Med. 69: 705–719.

Levine, B. B. (1963). Studies on the dimensions of the rabbit anti-benzylpenicilloyl antibody-combining sites. J. Exptl. Med. 117: 161–183.

Mage, R., and Kabat, E. A. (1963). Immunochemical studies on dextrans. III. The specificities of rabbit antidextrans. Further findings on antidextrans with 1,2 and 1,6 specificities. J. Immunol. 91: 633–640.

Maurer, P. H. (1963). Nature of antigenic determinants in proteins and synthetic polypeptides. Ann. N. Y. Acad. Sci. 103: 549–580.

Metzger, H., and Singer, S. J. (1963). Binding capacity of reductively fragmented antibodies to the 2,4-dinitrophenyl group. Science 142: 674–676.

Metzger, H., Wofsy, L., and Singer, S. J. (1964). The participation of A and B polypeptide chains in the active sites of antibody molecules. Proc. Natl. Acad. Sci. U. S. 51: 612–618.

Pappenheimer, A. M., Jr., Lundgren, H. P., and Williams, J. W. (1940). Studies on the molecular weight of diphtheria toxin, antitoxin, and their reaction products. J. Exptl. Med. 71: 247–262.

Pappenheimer, A. M., Jr., and Robinson, E. S. (1937). A quantitative study of the Ramon diphtheria flocculation reaction. J. Immunol. 32: 291–300.

Porter, E. F., and Pappenheimer, A. M., Jr. (1939). Antigen-antibody reactions between layers adsorbed on built-up stearate films. J. Exptl. Med. 69: 755–765.

Pressman, D. (1957). Discussion following Dr. Kabat's paper. J. Cellular Comp. Physiol. 50: Suppl. 1, 97.

Pressman, D., and Roholt, O. (1961). Isolation of peptides from an antibody site. Proc. Natl. Acad. Sci. U. S. 47: 1606–1610.

Roholt, O., Radzimski, G., and Pressman, D. (1963). Antibody combining site—the B polypeptide chain. Science *141:* 726–727.

Sage, H. J., Deutsch, G. F., Fasman, G. D., and Levine, L. (1964). The serological specificity of the poly-alanine immune system. Immunochemistry *1:* 133–144.

Schoellman, G., and Shaw, E. (1962). A new method for labelling the active center of chymotrypsin. Biochem. Biophys. Res. Commun. *7:* 36–40.

Stollar, D., Levine, L., Lehrer, H. I., and Van Vunakis, H. (1962). The antigenic determinants of denatured deoxyribonucleic acid (DNA) reactive with lupus erythematosus serum. Proc. Natl. Acad. Sci. U. S. *48:* 874–880.

Talmage, D. W., and Cann, J. R. (1961). *The Chemistry of Immunity in Health and Disease*, Charles C Thomas (Springfield, Ill., 178 pp.) pp. 129–132.

Utsumi, S., and Karush, F. (1964). The subunits of purified rabbit antibody. Biochemistry *3:* 1329–1338.

Wofsy, L., Metzger, H., and Singer, S. J. (1962). Affinity labeling—a general method for labeling the active sites of antibody and enzyme molecules. Biochemistry *1:* 1031–1039.

6

The Valency of Antibodies

Although the general site properties of antibodies and enzymes are closely similar, two other general characteristics distinguish them from each other. The main distinction is that antibodies, unlike enzymes, do not ordinarily participate in synthetic and degradation processes involving the compounds bound to them. The other distinction is concerned with valency. Enzymes are usually regarded as univalent, i.e., molecules with single substrate-binding sites. In fact, chymotrypsin, with serine as an integral member of its binding site, is necessarily univalent since it possesses only one serine residue. Antibodies, on the other hand, are not limited to univalency, but can and most generally do possess at least two binding sites per molecule.

Immunochemists during the 1930's and 1940's and even into the 1950's were in somewhat of a quandary concerning the multivalency of antibodies. On the one hand, they found it difficult to explain precipitation reactions on the basis of univalency, and felt it was therefore most reasonable to accept Marrack's lattice hypothesis (1938) involving multivalency of both antibody and antigen. On the other hand, they found it difficult to believe "that the peptide chain of an antibody molecule during the short period of its formation, which may be only a few seconds, should always react with two identical determinant groups as templates, although other determinant groups were available." Haurowitz (1963), who wrote these words and who had earlier expressed his his concern over this point, continued as follows:

> The discovery of the univalence of the Fragments I and II and of their combination by a dithio bond suggests that the formation of I and II precedes their combination by an SS bridge and makes it unnecessary to postulate immunological bivalence of a single peptide chain.

Rothen and Landsteiner (1939) had proposed that the folding of a peptide chain of an antibody in many different ways could account for the large number of antigenic specificities, and Pauling (1940) used this concept in the formulation of his explanation of bivalency formation. He conceived of an antibody globulin as differing from normal globulin only in the two end parts of a coiled polypeptide chain. The two active ends by folding would first assume configurations complementary to an antigen surface and then one end would be freed. The central part of the protein would subsequently fold up into globular form and an antibody molecule with two oppositely placed active sites would result. From this description arose the familiar picture of a structurally rigid antibody molecule—an elongated ellipsoid with two bites symmetrically removed from the longitudinal ends.

From the material presented in Chapter 4 on the fragments of immunoglobulins, one can readily see that the Pauling concept of bivalent antibody structure is inaccurate in several ways. It was a remarkable concept for 1940, but its acceptance as a substantially accurate model by others during the subsequent two decades influenced immunochemical thinking to such a degree that many more years will pass before it will lose its hold. For example, Pressman, Grossberg, Roholt, Stelos, and Yagi (1963), in their discussions of the chemical nature of antibody molecules, suggested that the formation of univalent fragments against the same antigenic moiety, before union as bivalent entity, might perhaps follow the 1940 mechanism proposed by Pauling.

It is possible that Pressman et al. (1963) really meant to incorporate only that part of the Pauling concept that was borrowed from Rothen and Landsteiner into their proposal—the part concerning the folding of peptide chains about antigenic determinants. If so, there could be little argument. To incorporate the other parts would be to accept essentially a concept of a single-chain polypeptide with active sites placed symmetrically at the terminal ends. These latter are hardly commensurate with the modern concept, based on fact, of a multichain immunoglobulin with the bivalent active sites non-terminal in the unfolded form of the molecule and asymmetrically placed and joined in the folded form. Although the modern concept may not necessarily fit all types of immunoglobulins it does accurately describe rabbit IgG, which the Pauling concept had purported to but does not do.

We still do not know the order in which the complete rabbit IgG is assembled and therefore cannot assume that active sites are necessarily formed in univalent fragments and then later joined to form bivalent material, although this is a most inviting hypothesis. One logical order of assemblage would be as follows: (1) formation of an active site during the synthesis of an Fd-fragment (that portion of the heavy chain, called the A piece by Fleischman, Porter, and Press, 1963, that carries the bulk of antibody-site activity); (2) union of the Fd-fragments with a light chain to confer structural stability to the site (with selection of the various available forms of light chains based upon final conformation of the Fd-fragment); (3) union of two univalent fragments to form a bivalent piece; (4) union of the bivalent piece with a dimer of the Fc-fragment (similar to the 5S heavy-chain fragments found in new-born pigs and in the heavy-chain diseases of humans that were discussed in Chapter 4). Several orders of assemblage would be equally likely at the present time, and this one is offered only to exemplify the multistage processes that are possible. This particular order of assemblage does take cognizance of the natural occurrence of light chains and of dimers of Fc-fragments and assumes that these are synthesized independent of active-site formation. However, it is recognized that the natural occurrence of fragments does not necessarily indicate that the fragments have been synthesized as such—they may represent degraded forms of previously intact globulins, and degradation processes are not always the mere reverse of synthetic ones. (Perhaps the finding of dimers of Fc-fragments in the new-born pig offers the strongest suggestion in favor of the independent synthesis of the inactive immunoglobulin fragments.)

Can fully formed immunoglobulins exist with only univalent sites? The answer is a categorical "yes." Palmer and Nisonoff (1964) *created* such species by dissociating anti-ovalbumin and normal rabbit IgG separately into half-molecules (each half with an intact light and heavy chain) under mild conditions of reduction followed by acidification, and by mixing the univalent subunits of the antibody globulin with the inactive subunits of the normal globulin. Hybrid species of whole globulin with univalent antibody sites were obtained when the mixture was neutralized and recombination took place. Hong, Palmer, and Nisonoff (1965) investigated the system further, confirmed that the recombination of the various subunits was random (A-A, A-N, N-N), and showed that when the proportion of antibody (A) subunits to normal (N) subunits was 1:11 the amount of A-A formed was not enough to cause precipitation of added ovalbumin although full retention of binding to ovalbumin was retained. Fully formed immunoglobulins with mixed specificity can also be formed by recombination of subunits directed against two different antigens. Such hybrids are essentially bivalent, but univalent with respect to individual antigens. Jacot-Guillarmond and Isliker (1962) demonstrated such an effect in the case of *human 19S IgM* by obtaining hybrids with both anti-A and anti-B isoagglutinating activity!

In a parallel manner the bivalent 5S fragments of antibodies from rabbit IgG, which are still precipitable with antigens, can be reduced to univalent fragments, mixed with univalent fragments of other antibodies, and recombined to form hybrid 5S fragments (Nisonoff and Rivers 1961; Nisonoff and Mandy, 1962; Seth, Nisonoff, and Dray, 1965). The recombination here also takes place in a random manner. Although the quantitative studies involving protein precipitation and hapten binding actually offer the most exacting evidence for hybridization, the direct visualization of hybrid formation is convincingly found in the work of Fudenberg, Drews, and Nisonoff (1964). Erythrocytes of two different species that could be distinguished from each other microscopically when mixed were further distinguishable by containing separate and different antigens upon their surface. Rabbit antibody against the one antigen would cause agglutination of red cells from only one species and this could be seen as clumped cells in the microscopic field. When and only when hybrid 5S bivalent fragments were formed from a mixture of univalent fragments from the two antibodies and added to a mixture of red cells from the two different species, mixed agglutination of both types of cells in the same clumps occurred (Figure 18). A mixture of the intact unhybridized 5S fragments also caused agglutination of both types of red cells but only in individual clumps that contained either one red cell species or the other, but not both.

It would not be surprising to find an occasional hybrid antibody in nature (if multivalent antibodies are indeed formed in nature from univalent subunits) either as a univalent species hybridized with a normal subunit or as a bivalent antibody with mixed specificity, but identity of such entities would require extremely careful work. The tendency may now be for some investigators to invoke the univalent hybrid as redress for their failure to demonstrate a precipitating antibody, but such a hybrid would not be expected to constitute any but an extremely small part of a total antibody preparation. Bivalency may be one important criterion for precipitin formation but it is by no means the only one, and the cautionary words of Kabat (1961) remain in force:

> While the evidence for the bivalence of certain precipitating antibodies is very strong, the tendency of numerous workers to infer that antibodies which fail to precipitate are *ipso facto* univalent is to be deplored.

This is borne out beautifully by Klinman, Rockey, Frauenberger, and Karush (1966), who showed that their equine non-precipitating IgA antibody was indeed bivalent.

In the next two chapters discussion of antibody reactions with haptens will first be taken up, followed by that of antigen-antibody reactions that result in precipitation. Discussions of valency at one time were out-

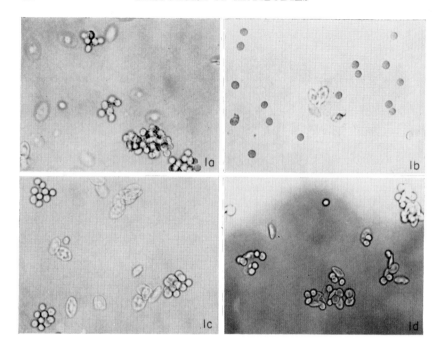

Fig. 18. Agglutinates made with chicken red cells coated with bovine γ-globulin and with human red cells coated with egg albumin by various bivalent 5S fragments of rabbit antibody: *1a*, anti-EA; *1b*, anti-BGG; *1c*, mixture of anti-EA and anti-BGG; *1d*, hybrid preparation of anti-EA and anti-BGG. Note that mixed agglutination occurs only with hybrid molecules. (Fudenberg, Drews, and Nisonoff, 1964.)

comes of these considerations, not preliminary to them. The study by Eisen and Karush (1949) established through equilibrium dialysis experiments that rabbit antibodies in equilibrium with their haptens were probably bivalent, and this first definitive work was substantiated by a number of workers. A study by Singer and Campbell (1953) established that rabbit antibodies in a complex solution of preformed antigen-antibody precipitates, redissolved by and in equilibrium with excess free antigen, were also most probably bivalent. Since one can now accept bivalence as the usual nature of rabbit IgG, as established so well by recent structural studies, one can turn things about and discuss with greater confidence and in converse fashion the assumptions that these workers needed to make in order to arrive at their conclusions of bivalence. This in turn can strengthen the use of such assumptions in areas other than bivalence where their application is *à propos*.

The possibility of the existence of multivalent states higher than the bivalent form is recognized by most immunochemists although definitive data are lacking at this writing. Hong, Palmer, and Nisonoff (1965) wondered, in fact, if perhaps a small amount of 10S material in their hybrid antibody preparations might contain molecules with more than two combining sites. They noted that such multivalent antibodies would substantially increase lattice formation in the precipitin reaction. Onoue, Yagi, Grossberg, and Pressman (1965) isolated a rabbit IgM with anti-Rp activity that is hexavalent. Reduction of the immunoglobulin to 6S subunits followed by alkylation showed that over 80% of the subunits were active. Thus multivalency is an intriguing open question that will bear considerable scrutiny in the near future, for its answer will obviously affect further detailing of structural and functional models of the immunoglobulins.

REFERENCES

Eisen, H. N., and Karush, F. (1949). The interaction of purified antibody with homologous hapten. Antibody valence and binding constant. J. Am. Chem. Soc. *71*: 363–364.

Fleischman, J. B., Porter, R. R., and Press, E. M. (1963). The arrangement of the peptide chains in γ-globulin. Biochem. J. *88*: 220–228.

Fudenberg, J., Drews, G., and Nisonoff, A. (1964). Serologic demonstration of dual specificity of rabbit bivalent hybrid antibody. J. Exptl. Med. *119*: 151–166.

Haurowitz, F. (1963). *The Chemistry and Function of Proteins*, 2nd Ed., Academic Press (New York, 455 pp.) p. 377.

Hong, R., Palmer, J. L., and Nisonoff, A. (1965). Univalence of half-molecules of rabbit antibody. J. Immunol. *94*: 603–610.

Jacot-Guillarmond, H., and Isliker, H. (1962). Scission et réassociation des isoagglutinines traitées par des agents réductens des ponts disulfures. Préparation d'anticorps mixtes. Vox Sanguinis *7*: 675–695.

Kabat, E. A. (1961). *Kabat and Mayer's Experimental Immunochemistry*, 2nd Ed., Charles C Thomas (Springfield, Ill., 905 pp.) p. 354.

Klinman, N. R., Rockey, J. H., Frauenberg, G., and Karush, F. (1966). Equine anti-hapten antibody. III. The comparative properties of γG- and γA-antibodies. J. Immunol. *96*: 587–595.

Marrack, J. R. (1938). *The Chemistry of Antigens and Anitbodies*. Her Majesty's Stationery Office (London, 194 pp.).

Nisonoff, A., and Mandy, W. J. (1962). Quantitative estimation of the hybridization of rabbit antibodies. Nature *194*: 355–359.

Nisonoff, A., and Rivers, M. M. (1961). Recombination of a mixture of univalent antibody fragments of different specificity. Arch. Biochem. Biophys. *93*: 460–462.

Onoue, K., Yagi, Y., Grossberg, A. L., and Pressman, D. (1965). Number of binding sites of rabbit macroglobulin antibody and its subunits. Immunochemistry *2*: 401–415.

Palmer, J. L., and Nisonoff, A. (1964). Hybridization of half molecules of rabbit gamma globulin. Science *143:* 376–379.

Pauling, L. (1940). A theory of the structure and process of formation of antibodies. J. Am. Chem. Soc. *62:* 2643–2657.

Pressman, D., Grossberg, A. L., Roholt, O., Stelos, P., and Yagi, Y. (1963). The chemical nature of antibody molecules and their combining sites. Ann. N. Y. Acad. Sci. *103:* 582–594.

Rothen, A., and Landsteiner, K. (1939). Adsorption of antibodies by egg albumin films. Science *90:* 65–66.

Seth, S. K., Nisonoff, A., and Dray, S. (1965). Hybrid molecules of rabbit γ-globulin formed by recombination of half-molecules of γ-globulins differing in genotype at two loci. Immunochemistry *2:* 39–50.

Singer, S. J., and Campbell, D. H. (1953). Physical chemical studies of soluble antigen-antibody complexes. II. Equilibrium properties. J. Am. Chem. Soc. *75:* 5577–5578.

PART TWO *Reactions of Antibodies*

7
Antibody Reactions with Haptens

1. Definition of a hapten

The word *hapten*, in its original Greek verb form, means *to touch, to grasp*, and *to fasten*. No other single word can describe in such an exquisitely simple manner the whole process of binding of an antigenic determinant with an antibody binding site. Many variations in the definition of a hapten have arisen since the word was first used by Landsteiner in 1921 (to refer to simple organic residues that react specifically with antibodies), but none describe so well what is really meant as the original Greek meaning.

One definition is immunobiological and attempts to describe haptens as substances which in themselves are incapable of inducing antibody formation in animals, but which, when attached to ordinary immunogens such as proteins and polysaccharides, can induce antibodies against themselves. Such a definition requires extensive qualification, for immunogenicity itself is a variable and is not always related to the size of the immunogen. For example, Maurer, Subrahmanyann, Katchalski, and Blout (1959) found that homopolymers of either poly-L-lysine or poly-L-glutamic acid were not in themselves antigenic in rabbits and guinea pigs whereas random copolymers of L-lysine and L-glutamic acid produced antibodies in both species of animals. Not even the copolymer, however, would produce antibodies in man (Maurer, Gerulat, and Pinchuck, 1962), and a third amino acid such as alanine or tyrosine was required for human immunogenicity. When "haptens" were attached to homopolymers of poly-L-lysine the immunogenic effect was the same in guinea pigs as if copolymers had been used (Benacerraf, Ojeda, and Maurer, 1963). But not all guinea pigs would respond. It was then found that the trait of responsiveness was genetically determined, one inbred strain of guinea pig demonstrating immunological reactivity to the hapten poly-L-lysine conjugates in every case, another strain in none (Kantor, Ojeda, and Benacerraf, 1963; Levine, Ojeda, and Benacerraf, 1963). Schechter, Bauminger, Sela, Nachtigal, and Feldman (1964)

produced immunological tolerance in rabbits to human serum albumin
(HSA), demonstrated that such rabbits would not produce antibodies
to HSA when injected with HSA, and then showed that such rabbits
would produce antibodies to HSA if injected with HSA that was conjugated with polytyrosine (increasing the HSA tyrosine content from
4.3 to 10.5 % with 28 moles of additional tyrosine per protein molecule).
It is obvious from these various examples that an immunogenic definition
of hapten leads to more semantic confusion than is necessary. One would
be hard put in each case to determine, on the basis of immunogenicity,
what portion was actually haptenic and what part conferred full immunogenicity upon the other. In the last case one would be led to the *reductio
ad absurdum* that HSA was just as haptenic as the polytyrosyl peptides
in the rabbit.

Another definition for a hapten is the severely limited one that confines
the term only to those distinctive chemical groupings that are artificially
conjugated to carrier structures. Such caution was understandable in
the early years of immunochemistry since the nature of antibody reactivity with macromolecules such as proteins and polysaccharides was
not understood in terms of active-site reactivity with small groupings
on the surfaces of the large molecular carriers. The definition became
loosened somewhat with the advent of lipid immunochemistry, wherein
it became apparent that such distinctive natural antigens as Forssman
and cardiolipin were in themselves relatively small compounds. Immunogenicity was conferred upon them by proteins and other substances
with which they formed non-specific complexes. Yet, although the use
of the term *lipid hapten* came into acceptable prominence to describe
a multitude of naturally occurring compounds, the term *protein hapten*
continued to be shunned. When it became apparent that the serological
specificity of polysaccharides was dependent upon the structure and
arrangement of a relatively small number of sugar residues and finally
that the reactivity of proteins with antibodies was due to the spatial
arrangement of a relatively small number of amino acid residues, it did
not, however, become less unpopular to use the terms *oligosaccharide*
and *peptide haptens*. Instead, the term *determinant group* came into
active usage. In modern usage *hapten* and *determinant group* are synon-
ymous.

To avoid confusion with the synthetic terminology necessary to
describe immunogenicity and yet to stretch the usage of hapten to the
full extent of its analytical meaning, the following simple definition
contains the necessary essence:

> A hapten is that specific chemical grouping to which a single
> antibody site conforms and with which it reacts.

A corollary to this definition is a postulate which is basic to the processes of hapten inhibition and antigen neutralization:

> As long as a hapten occupies an antibody site no other hapten can occupy the same site.

A second corollary that is obvious but nevertheless needs to be stated refers to the physical state of a hapten:

> A hapten, whether free and soluble or attached to a carrier in an exposed position, will react with an antibody site.

2. The law of mass action and equilibrium dialysis

The law of mass action as generally applied to the binding of free hapten with antibody requires the assumption that antibody combining sites on each antibody molecule function independently of each other, i.e., that they function as if they were on individual monovalent molecules. Nisonoff and Woernley (1959) offered the first direct evidence that this was a safe assumption to make. The equilibrium reached when radioactive p-iodobenzoate (Xpi) and bivalent anti-p-azobenzoate (anti-Xpz) were studied together under conditions of equilibrium dialysis was very similar to the equilibrium between Xpi and univalent anti-Xpz fragments. The concentration of hapten bound by the univalent fragments was only 6 % lower than that bound by the intact bivalent protein, a difference surprisingly close in view of the losses in site activity expected during fragmentation.

An equation can be written for the univalent fragments (F) and their interaction with hapten (H):

$$F + H \underset{k_r}{\overset{k_f}{\rightleftharpoons}} F\text{—}H$$

and, by the law of mass action, the association constant K_a can be obtained:

$$\frac{[F\text{—}H]}{[F]\,[H]} = \frac{k_f}{k_r} = K_a$$

$F\text{—}H$ represents bound hapten; H, free hapten, and F, hapten-free sites. Since the same equilibrium constant is assumed to hold for intact antibody, the equation can be written as

$$\frac{[H_b]}{(n[Ab] - [H_b])[H_f]} = K_b$$

where H_b = antibody-bound hapten, H_f = free hapten, n = antibody valence, $[Ab]$ = total antibody concentration, and $n\,[Ab] - [H_b]$ = concentration of antibody unoccupied by hapten.

In the process of equilibrium dialysis a measure of free hapten can be obtained since hapten is freely dialyzable whereas the bivalent antibody protein or the univalent fragments thereof is not. Thus, the value $[H_f]$ (or c as it is more usually called) is merely the concentration of hapten on the non-protein side of the dialyzing membrane. The value $[H_b]/[Ab]$ (or r as it is more usually called) represents the ratio of the bound hapten to the total antibody present. A measure of bound hapten in equilibrium dialysis is the difference in *concentrations* between total hapten on the protein side and total hapten on the non-protein side as measured by an analytical method specific for hapten. In the work of Nisonoff and Woernley just cited, radioisotope analysis was used.

In order to utilize the values c and r in the mass action formula, a rearrangement of the equation is necessary.

$$[H_b] = (n[Ab] - [H_b])[H_f]K_a$$

$$[H_b] = n[Ab][H_f]K_a - [H_b][H_f]K_a$$

$$\frac{[H_b]}{[Ab]} = n[H_f]K_a - \frac{[H_b]}{[Ab]}\,[H_f]K_a$$

$$r = ncK_a - rcK_a$$

$$\frac{r}{c} = nK_a - rK_a$$

This form is often referred to as the Scatchard (1949) form of the law of mass action. By plotting r/c against r a straight-line relationship is established in which both the valence and the equilibrium constant can be evaluated from slope and intercept data. Another form of the equation, emphasizing the similarity of hapten binding to adsorption phenomena, can be written in the style of the Langmuir adsorption isotherm:

$$\frac{1}{c} = \frac{nK_a}{r} - K_a$$

$$\frac{1}{r} = \left(\frac{1}{nK_a}\right)\left(\frac{1}{c}\right) + \frac{1}{n}$$

By plotting $1/r$ against $1/c$ a straight-line relationship is again established with a slope of $1/nK$ and an intercept of $1/n$.

The first attempt to determine an equilibrium constant for the binding of hapten to antibody was made by Marrack and Smith (1932) for the

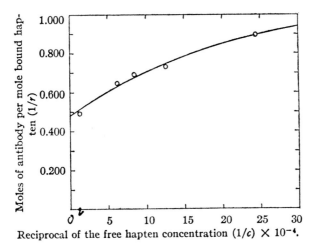

Fɪɢ. 19. Binding of an Rpz hapten by anti-Rpz as determined by equilibrium dialysis. (Eisen and Karush, 1949.)

reaction between the azo dye, p-phenylazobenzenearsonic acid, and antibody prepared in rabbits against arsanilic acid coupled to horse serum protein. This occasion was also the first application of the method of equilibrium dialysis to immunochemical problems. An association constant of $K_a = 1 \times 10^4$ M^{-1} was obtained, using arsenic analysis as the measure of free hapten concentration. The value should be considered only as a historical marker since the haptenic product could not be obtained in sufficient purity and since the extent of non-specific binding was not established. Haurowitz and Breinl (1933) controlled for non-specific binding by including normal serum in the outer dialysis phase when antiserum was in the inner. They also studied the binding of the weaker hapten, arsanilic acid. It was not until Eisen and Karush (1949) made a number of improvements in procedure that the process of equilibrium dialysis became fully applicable to obtaining thermodynamically acceptable data (Fig. 19). Purity of hapten was emphasized as was the use of purified antibody globulin to reduce non-specific effects. An equilibrium constant for the reaction between p-(p-hydroxyphenylazo)-benzenearsonic acid and antibody to p-azobenzenearsonic acid (anti-Rpz) was obtained:

$$K_a = 3.5 \times 10^5 \text{ M}^{-1}$$

With this directly obtained value it was then possible to estimate the free energy change ΔF associated with the equilibrium.

$$\Delta F = -RT \ln K_a$$
$$= -7.7 \text{ kcal/mole}$$

The valence n for the antibody was also obtained within 10%, corresponding to a value of 2.

3. Heterogeneity of binding sites

It became immediately apparent that linearity was not to be expected when data were plotted in the Scatchard or Langmuir forms even though extrapolations to obtain intercepts invariably indicated a valence of two. From this non-linearity arose the concept of binding-site heterogeneity since the linear form would hold only for homogeneous solutions with independently acting binding sites. We can see from the Nisonoff-Woernley data (1959) on independence of binding sites, as well as from the overwhelming amount of evidence already presented on heterogeneity, that the assumption of heterogeneity to explain non-linearity was a safe one to make. To correct for heterogeneity it is assumed that a continuous distribution of association constants exists, and that at each point in the distribution there is a homogeneous equilibrium between antibody and hapten (Karush, 1962) for which a given free energy state holds. If the distribution is Gaussian (normal), then a standard deviation σ of the distribution can be expressed. If the distribution follows a function such as that of Sips, then a different index of heterogeneity a is obtained (Nisonoff and Pressman, 1958a). The choice of distribution generally is made on the basis of ease of integration rather than upon actual knowledge of the distribution shape, but improvement in fitting theoretical curves to actual data is obtained regardless. The Gaussian form is more sensitive, the Sips is easier to integrate, and neither may be expressive of the actual distribution except as an approximation. Perhaps a better relation is that of Bowman and Aladjem (1963), in which no assumption concerning the distribution form is made.

In practice a standard value for an association constant (K_0) is obtained from that point where antibody sites are half-saturated with hapten, i.e., where there is an average of one bound hapten per bivalent antibody molecule, and, thus, where $r = 1$ and $n = 2$. From the Scatchard equation,

$$r/c = nK_a - rK_a$$
$$1/c = 2K_a - K_a = K_0$$

The association constant becomes the reciprocal of concentration at that point. (The standard association constant, of course, must be obtained at 25°C in keeping with accepted thermodynamic conditions.) Regardless of the degree of heterogeneity there is only a single value for K_0 where $cK_a = 1$ since all distributions are expressed in terms of the product cK_a. Each single homogeneous reaction within the distribution, whatever its nature, can be expressed by the fraction of the total combining sites (S) filled with hapten, i.e., $[H_b]/[F]$ or $[H_b]/n[Ab]$ or r/n or dS/S. From the law of mass action one can easily obtain

$$\frac{r}{n} = \frac{dS}{S} = \frac{cK_a}{1 + cK_a}$$

$$\frac{dS}{S} = \frac{1}{\dfrac{1}{cK_a} + 1}$$

$$\frac{dS}{S} = \frac{1}{(cK_a)^{-1} + 1}$$

which shows that the distribution of the fraction of filled combining sites at any point in the distribution is a function of the product of concentration and an association constant. For the total distribution, whatever its nature, the function must express what happens to the product, but at $cK_a = 1$ the function becomes $\frac{1}{2}$. The concentration c obtained by analysis at this point represents the average concentration of the many discrete homogeneous c values; therefore, K_a at this point is the average equilibrium constant regardless of the type of distribution.

The easiest linear form of the homogeneous mass action law from which to demonstrate heterogeneity stems from the reciprocal relation n/r since

$$\frac{n}{r} = \frac{1 + cK_a}{cK_a}$$

$$\frac{n}{r} = \frac{1}{cK_a} + 1$$

This was the plot form used by Karush and Sonnenberg (1949) to evaluate σ by curve fitting and was used by Nisonoff and Pressman (1958) to develop the Sips distribution function:

$$\frac{n}{r} = \frac{S}{dS} = \frac{1}{(cK_0)^a} + 1$$

$$\frac{1}{dS} = \frac{1}{b} = \frac{1}{(cK_0)^a S} + \frac{1}{S}$$

where b was the fraction of bound hapten, c the fraction of free hapten,

a the heterogeneity index, K_0 the average standard association constant, and S the total available number of binding sites. To obtain the best value of the heterogeneity index, $1/b$ was plotted against $1/(c)^a$ until an a value was obtained which would give the best linear plot. In the cases of p-iodobenzoate and p-(p-hydroxyphenylazo)benzoate, a values of 0.7 and 0.75 were obtained, respectively, in their reactions with a single antibody preparation against p-azobenzoate (anti-Xpz). The curved and linear plots are shown in Figures 20 and 21 (Nisonoff and Pressman, 1958b).

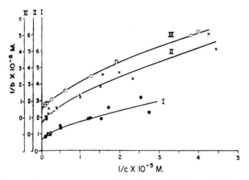

FIG. 20. Binding of haptens by specifically purified anti-Xpz at 5° ± 0.1°C in saline-borate buffer, pH 8, μ = 0.16. Curve I, p-(p'-hydroxyphenylazo)benzoate; curve II, labeled p-iodobenzoate; III, labeled p-iodobenzoate with a second antibody. (Nisonoff and Pressman, 1958b.)

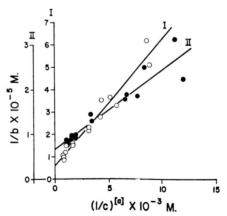

FIG. 21. Binding of haptens by specifically purified antibody. Curve I, labeled p-iodobenzoate, $[a]$ = 0.7; curve II, p-(p'-hydroxyphenylazo)benzoate, $[a]$ = 0.75. (Nisonoff and Pressman, 1958b.)

The heterogeneity index would be more useful if it were a single-valued constant for a given hapten-antihapten reaction. However, *there is as much if not more heterogeneity among heterogeneity indices than there is among average equilibrium constants* and free energy changes calculated from them. Among five individual rabbits immunized and reacting with the same hapten, Nisonoff and Pressman (1958a) obtained five separate values for a ranging from 0.65 to 1.0, but with $-\Delta F^\circ$ values falling within the range 5.6–6.2 kcal/mole.

A review of heterogeneity would appear to be in order at this juncture according to Singer's (1964) classification:

Class heterogeneity—heavy chain distinctions and distributions of activity among various immunoglobulins

Intrachain heterogeneity—for a given immunoglobulin, variations in tertiary structures that are supportive of combining sites but that are not directly involved in the sites themselves

Site heterogeneity—variations in combining sites themselves

Singer added a fourth type of heterogeneity which had previously gone unrecognized: *structural heterogeneity*. He conceived of haptenic groups, themselves, not as homogeneous entities but as surface constituents capable of taking on a wide spectrum of structures depending on carrier environment. Some would protrude outwards from the surface; others, at the other extreme, would lie embedded in a protein surface in van der Waals contact with a constellation of amino acid residues. These embedded haptens with their amino acid vestments would form new antigenic determinants—*hybrid haptens*. In the polypeptide-protein conjugate series, polyglutamyl groups would be expected to protrude because of their hydrophilic ionizable properties whereas polyleucyl and polyphenylalanyl groups would be more likely to form hybrid haptens because of their hydrophobic nature. Viewing the results of Stahmann, Lapresle, Buchanan-Davidson, and Grabar (1959) and those of Buchanan-Davidson, Dellert, Kornguth, and Stahmann (1959) with this picture in mind, Singer readily explained the discrepancies in their work. Immunization with polyglutamyl-bovine serum albumin resulted in antibodies that could be completely absorbed out by separate absorptions with bovine serum albumin and with polyglutamyl-rabbit serum albumin conjugate. However, immunization with polyleucyl- or polyphenylalanyl-bovine serum albumin resulted in antibodies of which 23–42 % could *not* be absorbed out by separate absorptions with bovine serum albumin and with polyleucyl- or polyphenylalanyl-rabbit serum albumin. The remaining antibodies, easily absorbable by the homologous hapten protein conjugate, were very likely directed against hybrid antigens.

To obtain a homogeneous preparation of antihapten antibody with limited or no heterogeneity would seem to pose a number of difficult problems, but the use of non-hybridizable haptens would perhaps lessen the problems. It is Singer's belief (1964) that such preparations "may well be necessary for the ultimate determination of the detailed chemical structure of antibody molecules."

4. Kinetics of the hapten-antibody reaction

When Berson and Yalow (1959) reported that the association constant for human anti-insulin with insulin could apparently be as high as $K_0 = 1 \times 10^9$ M^{-1}, there was considerable doubt in many circles that this high binding should be attributed to an antigen-antibody reaction alone. Perhaps some other factor in the human serum had contributed to the binding and brought it to equilibrium far to the right of the ordinary reaction. The reason for such skepticism was partially contained in the Pauling theory of 1940, in which a rather narrow range of values, 10^4–10^6 M^{-1}, was predicted. The upper limit would be necessary to permit dissociation of the formed antibody from its cell-bound antigen and allow it to enter the circulation. The lower limit, if any lower, would indicate binding so poor as to be ineffective in specificity discrimination except in cases of high antigenic valency. [Concerning this last point, note that the intrinsic equilibrium constant K_H for the reaction of haptens with individual antibody sites is related to the extrinsic equilibrium constant K_{Ab} for the reaction of multivalent antigen with bivalent antibody by the relation $K_{Ab} = mK_H/2$ where m = the valency of antigen (cf. Singer and Campbell, 1953).]

In the same year that Talmage (1960) reported another high association constant, 5×10^8, for serum albumin and its antibody (which also could conceivably have been attributed to an impurity), Velick, Parker, and Eisen (1960) measured high binding in an elegant and unambiguous way and, by so doing, proved that another of the conditions of the Pauling theory need not be met. They utilized the method of tryptophan fluorescence quenching as the basis of their technique, and showed that tryptophan residues of intact antibody molecules and of univalent fragments gave a fluorescence quantum yield diminished by 70% when reacted with their conforming hapten, ϵ-N-DNP-lysine (formed from 2,4-dinitrophenol and the ϵ-amino groups of lysine). An equilibrium constant of 2×10^8 M^{-1} at 26°C was obtained along with a standard free energy change of -8.6 kcal/mole. Incidental to the study was the finding that the fluorescence-quenching properties of the individual antibody sites of intact antibody molecules were additive, thus showing that the binding properties of one were not affected by the other. Separate non-overlapping domains of eight to nine tryptophan residues were implicated.

The time was now ripe for kinetic studies, and the ingenuity of a few graduate students under Sehon at McGill and Singer at Yale gave rise to some exceedingly important and fundamental results. The requirements for a successful kinetic study were set down by L. A. Day, Sturtevant, and Singer (1963): (1) The antigen-antibody system must be well defined, the concentration of reactions must be accurately determined, and the reversible bimolecular reactions must be distinguishable from reversible aggregation reactions. (2) The combination of antigen with antibody must result in a kinetically correlated and accurately measurable change in some property of the system. (3) The means of measurement of the change in property must be capable of following the change over extremely short time intervals.

The cathode-ray polarographic technique of Schneider and Sehon (1961) for following the reaction of rabbit antibodies with p-(p-amino-phenylazo)phenylarsonic acid fulfilled the first two criteria but not the last. The hapten as a free molecule was detectable as a reducible azo group at the mercury cathode of a polarograph but, when bound to antibody, was not available. Thus, free hapten could be measured in terms of peak heights on an oscilloscope at intervals of 1 sec in the micromolar range. The time intervals were still not short enough and, although an equilibrium constant was easily obtained (6.15×10^5 M^{-1}), the forward reaction could not be evaluated.

Sehon's group then turned to a temperature-jump relaxation method (Froese, Sehon, and Eigen, 1962) in which rapid reactions involving changes in heat of reaction (enthalpic changes) could be followed in microsecond intervals. A condenser was discharged through a conducting solution containing the reaction mixture and in 0.1–1 μsec created a temperature jump of about 10°C. The reaction mixture was then measured as it adjusted to the new conditions brought on by the perturbation, and the time taken to reach the new equilibrium was obtained from oscillographic recordings. This time, called relaxation time τ, was found by derivation (Eigen and De Maeyer, 1962) to be related to the forward and reverse reaction rate constants of the new equilibrium by

$$1/\tau = k_r + k_f([\text{Ab}] + [H])$$

where [Ab] and [H] were antibody and hapten concentrations at the new equilibrium. The third criterion for a good kinetic study would thereby be met but now a suitable hapten was required to meet the first two criteria. One such hapten was the dye molecule, 1-naphthol-4-[4-(4'-azobenzeneazo)phenylarsonic acid], which would undergo a spectral shift to longer wave lengths when binding with antibody took place (Sehon, 1963). Through controlled assays and spectrophotometric determinations a forward reaction rate constant, $k_f = 2 \times 10^7 \text{ M}^{-1} \text{ sec}^{-1}$, and a reverse reaction rate constant, $k_r = 50 \text{ sec}^{-1}$, were obtained. The equilibrium constant was $K_0 = 4 \times 10^5 \text{ M}^{-1}$. In the case of interaction of specific rabbit antibodies with the p-nitrobenzene derivative, 4,5-dihydroxy-3-(p-nitrophenylazo)-2,7-naphthalenedisulfonate, Froese and Sehon (1965) obtained a spectral shift from 515 to 530 mμ. Through the temperature-jump relaxation-time method, forward and reverse rate constants of $1.8 \times 10^8 \text{ M}^{-1} \text{ sec}^{-1}$ and $7.6 \times 10^2 \text{ sec}^{-1}$ were obtained along with an equilibrium constant of $2.4 \times 10^5 \text{ M}^{-1}$.

The instrumentation developed by Sturtevant in Singer's laboratory for rapid measurements was a thermostated stopped-flow recorder in which reactants could be mixed during flow in a special mixing chamber and brought to rest in a quartz observation tube, all in 0.003 sec (cf. L. A. Day, Sturtevant, and Singer, 1963). The reaction could then be followed fluorometrically or spectrophotometrically as a function of time after mixing and instantaneously recorded. One of the haptens that was used for which kinetically correlated and accurately measurable data could be obtained was 2-(2,4-dinitrophenylazo)-1-naphthol-3,6-disulfonic acid, in which marked spectral shifts would occur upon binding with antibody specific for dinitrophenyl groups (anti-DNP). A forward reaction rate constant, $k_f = 8.0 \times 10^7 \text{ M}^{-1} \text{ sec}^{-1}$, and a reverse reaction rate constant, $k_r = 1.4 \text{ sec}^{-1}$, were obtained, giving an equilibrium constant of $K_0 = 5.9 \times 10^7 \text{ M}^{-1}$. As pointed out in a previous chapter, the reaction of antibody with DNP hapten was seen to be one of the fastest bimolecular reactions on record in immunochemistry. Similar data were obtained for DNP-lysine and DNP-aminocaproate, the latter showing $k_f = 1.0 \times 10^8 \text{ M}^{-1} \text{ sec}^{-1}$, $k_r = 1.1 \text{ sec}^{-1}$, and $K_0 = 9.1 \times 10^7$ M^{-1}. Froese and Sehon (1965), in studying the reaction of anti-NP (rabbit antibodies to the mononitro determinant, p-nitrophenyl) with DHNDS-NP [4,5-dihydroxy-3-(p-nitrophenylazo)-2,7-naphthalenedisulfonic acid disodium salt], obtained $1.8 \times 10^8 \text{ M}^{-1} \text{ sec}^{-1}$ for k_f, 760 sec^{-1} for k_r, and $5.8 \times 10^5 \text{ M}^{-1}$ for K_0. Here was an example not only of an even faster forward reaction but also of a faster dissociation, resulting in an equilibrium constant of moderate value within the range set by Pauling.

Fluorescence polarization, another technique for discriminating between free and bound hapten by measuring the change in direction of polarization in three dimensions as hapten becomes bound to antibody, gave an equilibrium constant $K_0 = 2.11 \times 10^8$ M^{-1} for the reaction of anti-fluorescein-ovalbumin (anti-FO) with FO (Dandliker, Schapiro, Meduski, Alonso, Feigen, and Hamrick, 1964), but only 5.4×10^6 M^{-1} for anti-FO with fluorescein. Amkraut (1964), using a technique of fluorescence enhancement in which rhodamine-DNP showed increased fluorescence during binding with antibody, obtained equilibrium constants approaching 1×10^8 M^{-1} as immunization continued. In combination with proper timing devices these two additional techniques would provide further means for measuring the rates of association and dissociation of hapten-antibody combinations.

Referring not only to his own technique of fluorescence enhancement but also to the whole general method of detecting molecular shifts in excitation energies that result from binding, Winkler (1962) called such haptens "molecular probes" because of their intimate association with binding site-topology and reactivity. Eisen had used the term earlier to refer to haptens in general, but in kinetic studies the use of "molecular probes" seems particularly fitting. It would appear that with these most recent molecular probes investigators have shown that one of the necessary preconditions of the Pauling theory—an upper limit for K_0 of 10^6—has not been met. To this author such revelations as equilibrium constants that are two orders of magnitude higher than the Pauling limit mean that the initial formation of antibody *in vivo* most probably was *not* made around a haptenic template and that some synthetic theory other than that of Pauling is needed to account for free antibody with high binding characteristics. As mentioned earlier the rate of reaction between hapten and antibody can be so rapid that it approaches the rate of diffusion of the reactants themselves and in some cases is evidently controlled by diffusion as the rate-limiting step. It is conceivable, therefore, that the upper limit of reaction rates has not been measured and that therefore the highest negative free-energy changes have not been recognized. Eisen and Pearce (1962), in fact, raised the possibility that high binding antibody might be eliminated preferentially in hyperimmunized animals. Eisen and Siskind (1964) then reinforced such a concept with very convincing experimental evidence. It was felt that complexes between high binding antibody and excessive antigen would form and result in immune elimination from the circulation. Since the evidence was based on the *absence* of high binding antibody in hyperimmunized animals, not on its direct measurement, alternative explanations could, of course, be constructed as Eisen and Siskind pointed out. Such an immune elimination process, in itself, would seriously affect the type of antiserum reagent obtained, its heterogeneity characteristics, and its average association constant. Thus, in rabbits receiving only 5 mg of DNP-bovine γ-globulin (BGG), the average K_0 rose from 0.8×10^6 M^{-1} at 2 weeks to as high as 2.5×10^8 M^{-1} at 8 weeks, whereas in rabbits receiving 250 mg the average K_0 remained at 0.2×10^6 M^{-1} during the whole period.

In keeping with the theme of heterogeneity which permeates immunochemistry there is also kinetic heterogeneity. Molecules in a given population of antibodies may vary greatly in forward and reverse reaction rate constants, thus affecting the heterogeneity index of the equilibrium between hapten and antibody site. From one antiserum to another there is heterogeneity among the average rate and equilibrium constants, and no constant can be assigned to a particular hapten-antibody reaction that can be expected to hold for all antisera against the hapten. There is probably even greater kinetic heterogeneity in nature than is revealed in the few literature reports since it is more the practice to screen a large number of antisera for those few with the greatest potency than it is to make measurements on sera at random. The data of Eisen and Siskind (1964), showing 100- to 200-fold increases in equilibrium constants for individual rabbits from the second to the eighth week following immunization with small doses of antigen, rather emphasize the point that even for multiple sera from a single animal uniformity in average equilibrium constants cannot be expected. The data of Klinman, Rockey, Frauenberger, and Karush (1966) reinforce this point even further. In a single horse with anti-Lac antibody activity distributed among six different immunoglobulins, these authors found that the association constant K_A at 6 weeks after injection was, for example, 10^5 M^{-1} for IgG and greater than 10^7 M^{-1} for IgA. After 6 months K_A for both globulins was greater than 10^7 M^{-1}. Scatchard plots for 2-week to 20-week sera were precise, unequivocal, and most convincing.

5. Haptenic cross-reactivity and specificity, and the nature of the forces involved

Although much of the early work on haptenic cross-reactivity and specificity involved techniques of hapten inhibition, as developed by Landsteiner, much more meaningful data were obtained through direct studies of hapten binding. Inhibition methods involved a second step such as precipitation: the more hapten inhibition, the less antigen reactivity, and the less precipitation, etc. Criticism of this method appears in Chapter 9. Equilibrium dialysis, as has been pointed out, has become a central technique for the study of hapten binding.

One of the most forceful early experiments to indicate the sensitivity and specificity of the immunochemical reaction was that of Landsteiner and van der Scheer (1928) on the differentiation between the optical isomers of phenyl-(p-aminobenzoylamino)acetic acid (Ip).

D-Ip   L-Ip

Antisera against the azoprotein of the one stereoisomer would distinguish it from the other.

By the process of equilibrium dialysis Karush (1956, 1958) made a detailed study of the reaction of antibody with these haptenic isomers. Antibody was prepared in rabbits against the haptens, coupled to bovine IgG, and was tested against the haptens, coupled to dimethylaniline. The extra group was attached to the test antigens to provide intensely visible absorption bands with which concentrations as dilute as 10^{-5} M could be detected spectrophotometrically.

Isomeric D-Ip conjugated to dimethylaniline (D-Ip-azo dye)

Binding results of D-Ip with two different anti-D-Ip antibodies at two different temperatures are shown in Table 10.

The colorless p-nitro derivatives, homologous to the isomeric haptens,

TABLE 10

Binding Data of Two Different Anti-D-Ipz-Protein Antibodies for D-Ip-Azo Dye

Antibody No.	n	σ	25°C		7.1°C		$-\Delta H^0$	ΔS^0
			$10^5 K_0$	$-\Delta F^0$	$10^5 K_0$	$-\Delta F^0$		
			M^{-1}	kcal/mole	M^{-1}	kcal/mole	kcal/mole	e.u./mole
22	2.0	2.3	2.05	7.25	4.4	7.24	7.1	0.3
24	2.0	2.3	3.1	7.50	6.7	7.48	7.3	0.7

(From Karush, 1956, 1958.)

TABLE 11

Binding Data of an Anti-D-Ipz-Protein Antibody for Optical Isomers of p-Nitro-Ip

Compound	$10^5 K_0$	$-\Delta F^0$
	M^{-1}	kcal/mole
D-Ip-azo dye.............	2.94	7.48
p-Nitro-D-Ip.............	1.28	6.98
p-Nitro-L-Ip.............	0.00657	3.85

(From Karush, 1956, 1958.)

TABLE 12

Binding Data of an Anti-D-Ipz-Protein Antibody for Optical Isomers of Deaminated Ip

Compound	$10^5 K_0$	$-\Delta F^0$
	M^{-1}	kcal/mole
D-Ip-azo dye.............	2.94	7.48
D-Ip (deaminated).......	8.77	6.74
L-Ip (deaminated).......	2.08	5.90

(From Karush, 1956, 1958.)

were prepared and tested for their inhibition of the colored azohaptens. From the inhibition effects noted, binding data for the derivatives could be obtained. As can be seen in Table 11, p-nitro-D-Ip had an equilibrium constant for anti-D-Ip that was nearly ½ that of the D-Ip-azo dye whereas p-nitro-L-Ip, the optical isomer, had a constant that was only 1/400 that of the D-Ip-azo dye.

When the deaminated forms of the haptens (in terms of the original Landsteiner-van der Scheer haptens) were used as inhibitors, much greater cross-reactivity of the L-isomer for the anti-D-Ip and *vice versa* was observed than with the nitro compounds (Table 12).

D-Phenyl(benzoylamino)acetic acid (deaminated D-Ip)

Karush (1958) attributed the increase in cross-reactivity to a reversal of roles by the phenyl group of the benzoyl substituent and the α-phenyl group as to their location when bound to antibody.

These data from Karush, which are only briefly summarized, exemplify the type of thermodynamic information that can be obtained for the interaction of antibody with other than its homologous hapten. They indicate something of the nature of the spatial orientation and the binding force that enters into the nature of specificity. Forces that contribute to the usual ionic and covalent bonds are too strong to be considered since they may range from about 50 to 100 kcal/mole. Much weaker forces, those that would result in antigen-antibody bonds of 4–12 kcal/mole, are involved instead. Of the weak forces there are several possibilities:

> Coulombic forces between charged groups varying inversely as the square of the distance between groups
> Polar forces, including hydrogen bonds, that are present between non-ionic groups in which positive and negative centers appear as dipoles, varying inversely as the sixth power of the distance between groups;
> Van der Waals forces, of very short range, that are essentially attractive and compressive, varying inversely as the seventh power of interatomic distances

Single bonds between hapten and antibody sites would provide little stability, thereby necessitating several points of force contact, several weak bonds, for firm binding. But short-range forces necessitate complementarity. And arising from the multibonded short-range forces in complementarity comes specificity. The question that arises is whether antibody sites can at one time or another conceivably accommodate all nature of short-range forces in their reaction with haptens. Heterogeneity of site formation does make it appear possible that this should be so. There is experimental evidence to corroborate this hypothesis, e.g., in the experiments of Koshland and Englberger (1963) that were referred to in Chapter 5 and Table 9.

Antibodies were prepared in the same single rabbit against two different haptens, one with a negative charge (phenylarsonate or Rp) and the other with a positive charge (phenyltrimethylammonium or Ap). The antibodies were then separated by specific purification processes and analyzed for their respective amino acid compositions. The anti-Rp antibody contained more arginine and isoleucine, suggestive of side chains with a positive charge that would react with the negatively charged Rp, whereas the anti-Ap antibody contained more leucine and aspartic acid, suggestive of side chains were a reverse rôle. Naturally, the involvement of these side chains in the active sites of their respective antibodies cannot be taken for granted; as a matter of fact, it would be just as likely that the differences occurred in the light chains as in heavy chains, with selection of the particular amino acid side chains to balance the haptenic charge occurring after site synthesis.

The data of Grossberg and Pressman (1960) were presented as additional support for the hypothesis of differences in site topology depending upon the particular haptenic charge. Evidence was given that diazoacetamide (DAA), which alkylates only carboxyl groups, reduces the binding strength of anti-Ap by one-third to one-half. When anti-Ap is alkylated, while hapten is bound to it, antibody activity is preserved. When unprotected anti-Xp is alkylated with DAA no effect upon binding occurs. The authors felt that their findings provided clear-cut evidence that negatively charged carboxyl groups were in the anti-Ap but not anti-Xp site and that therefore the sites differed in amino acid composition. As was discussed in an earlier chapter, the classical protection type experiment upon which this work is based cannot be relied upon to give straightforward answers concerning site topology, and this was emphasized by the findings of Roholt and Pressman on the iodination of antibody sites (cf. Chapter 5.5). But whatever the effect of the haptenic charge upon antibody-site topology, it is clear that differences do exist between certain molecular portions of anti-Ap and anti-Xp antibodies. Affinity labeling would appear to be the best way to pin down any differences in site topology. As Singer (1965) pointed out, in commenting upon the DAA effects observed by Grossberg and Pressman (1960),

> This provides good evidence for a chemical difference between combining sites of two different specificities. It does not demonstrate, however, that one or more amino acid *substitutions* have occurred within common polypeptide sequences within the two sites ... The same carboxyl group(s) might be present in both anti-A$_p$ and anti-X$_p$ polypeptide chains, but in the former they might be in contact with the positively charged hapten, while in the latter they might be folded out of contact with the negatively charged hapten. Amino acid sequence studies can presumably settle this problem.

Studies with uncharged haptens, of course, show that the short-range coulombic forces, which may play a role in anti-Xp and anti-Ap reactions with their charged haptens, are not by any means the only ones available. For example, the data obtained by Karush (1957, 1958) for the uncharged disaccharide, p-azophenyl-β-lactoside (Lac), combined with

TABLE 13

Binding Data for Two Different Anti-Lac Antibodies and Lac-Dye

n	σ	25°C		7.1°C		$-\Delta H^0$	ΔS^0
		$10^5 K_0$	$-\Delta F^0$	$10^5 K_0$	$-\Delta F^0$		
		M^{-1}	kcal/mole	M^{-1}	kcal/mole	kcal/mole	e.u./mole
2.0	1.5	1.57	7.09	4.48	7.25	9.7	−8.8
2.0	1.5	1.04	6.85	2.90	7.01	9.7	−9.5

(From Karush, 1957, 1958.)

TABLE 14

Binding Data for an Anti-Lac Antibody and Various Haptens

Hapten*	$10^5 K_0$	$-\Delta F^0$
	M^{-1}	kcal/mole
Lac-dye..............................	1.34	7.00
p-nitrophenyl-β-lactoside...............	0.675	6.60
Methyl-β-lactoside.....................	0.202	5.88
Lactose (64% β).......................	0.110	5.52
Cellobiose (66% β)....................	0.000275	1.96
Methyl-β-D-galactoside................	0.000747	2.56
Methyl-α-D-galactoside...	0.000134	1.54
Methyl-β-D-glucoside..................	0.000051	0.97

(From Karush, 1957, 1958.)
* Structures:

Lac-dye

p-Nitrophenyl-β-lactoside

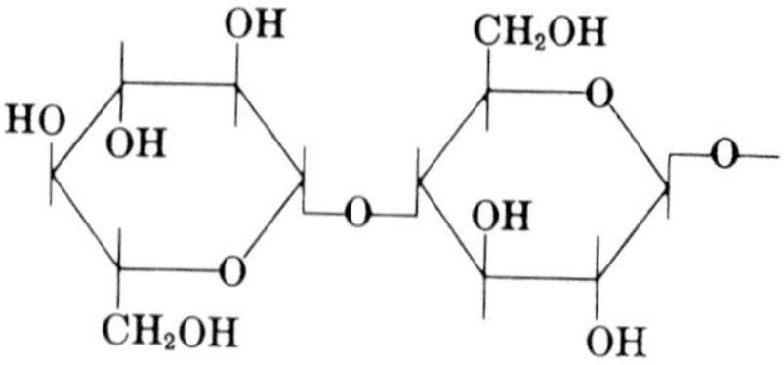

β-Cellobioside

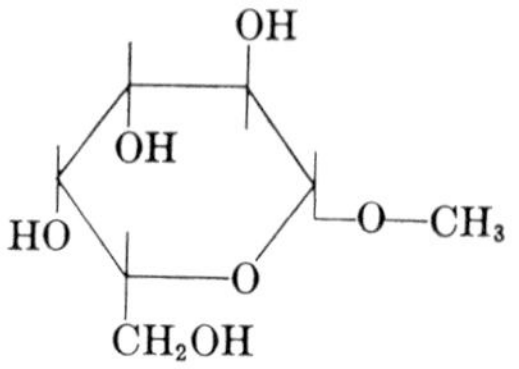

Methyl-β-D-galactoside

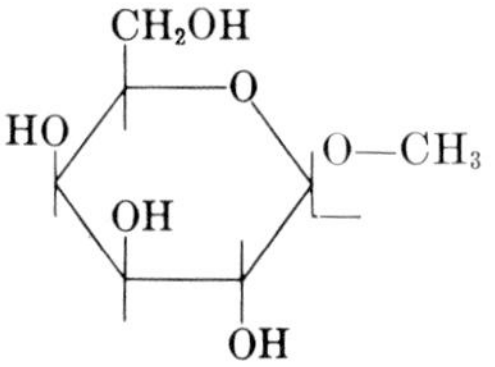

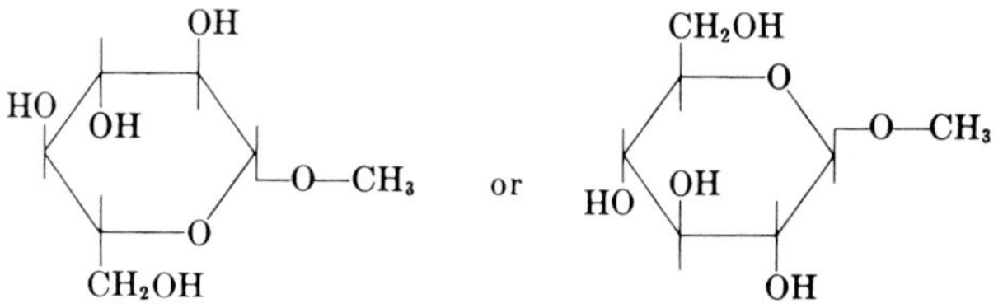

Methyl-α-D-galactoside

Methyl-β-D-glucoside

dimethyl-aniline to form Lac-azo dye, reveal as strong binding as those for anti-Ip (Table 13). Of particular interest is the larger value for $-\Delta H^0$, which is undoubtedly brought about by hydrogen bonding between the disaccharide and the conforming antibody site.

Cross-reactivities of anti-Lac antibody for other sugar derivatives are given in Table 14. The dominant structural feature that confers specificity is clearly the disaccharide portion of the complex hapten, and Karush (1957) estimates that the β-galactoside and β-glucoside units contribute 5 and 3 kcal/mole, respectively. Thus, although the terminal hexose may be slightly dominant, its partner in the disaccharide plays a major rôle in binding. From these considerations it would be difficult not to visualize hydrogen bonding as a major force in the short-range binding of Lac-anti-Lac. With a reversal of only the hydrogen and hydroxyl groups of carbon atom 4 in the terminal sugar residue, lactose becomes cellobiose. In so doing it loses 3.6 kcal in $-\Delta F^0$ of binding. The specificity for lactose, whatever the force involved, is indeed very striking. The original observations of Goebel, Avery, and Babers (1934) on the nature of the specificity and cross-reactivity in this system (using hapten inhibition of precipitation reactions) are thus completely borne out and extended by these experiments with free haptens and their antibodies in equilibrium.

6. Summary

Considerations of free haptens in simple equilibrium with haptens bound by antibody lead up to the more complex reactions, such as precipitation, that are to be discussed next. However, the complex reactions, regardless of the secondary or indirect effects that make them complex, still depend upon the primary reaction of a hapten with its antibody site. Although the sites of an individual antibody molecule are bivalent or multivalent and are similar in reactivity and specificity with each other, they do function quite independently. The haptens which they bind may be free or attached to artificial and natural carriers, but are bound with about the same force regardless of their state. Heterogeneity that permeates every aspect of hapten-antibody interaction necessitates standardization of each reagent serum, individual or pooled, before it can be reliably used for assays. The thermodynamic and kinetic characteristics of antibody sites are sensitive to shifts in heterogeneity, but are readily reproducible for a given antibody preparation in its repeated reactions with a given hapten. If it were not for this reproducibility, analytical immunochemistry would be impossible. Because of it and in spite of heterogeneity, analytical immunochemistry has been a highly useful science and not a mere curiosity for nearly half a century. In fact, because of heterogeneity the wide range of specific antibody reagents has been made possible. Through judicious employment of purification techniques, based upon a rational observance of hapten-antibody interactions, the range of analytical immunochemistry can readily be widened even further.

REFERENCES

Amkraut, A. A. (1964). Determination of antibody-hapten binding constant by fluorescence enhancement. Immunochemistry 1: 231–235.

Benacerraf, B., Ojeda, A., and Maurer, P. H. (1963). Studies on artificial antigens. II. The antigenicity in guinea pigs or arsanilic acid conjugates of copolymers of D- or L-α-amino acids. J. Exptl. Med. 118: 945–952.

Berson, S. A., and Yalow, R. S. (1959). Quantitative aspects of the reaction between insulin and insulin-binding antibody. J. Clin. Invest. *38:* 1996–2016.

Bowman, J. D., and Aladjem, F. (1963). A method for the determination of heterogeneity of antibodies. J. Theoret. Biol. *4:* 242–253.

Buchanan-Davidson, D., Dellert, E., Kornguth, S., and Stahmann, M. (1959). Immunochemistry of synthetic polypeptides and polypeptidyl proteins. II. Quantitative studies on the modified proteins. J. Immunol. *83:* 543–551.

Dandliker, W. B., Schapiro, H. C., Meduski, J. W., Alonso, R., Feigen, G. A., and Hamrick, J. R., Jr. (1964). Application of fluorescence polarization to the antigen-antibody reaction. Immunochemistry *1:* 165–191.

Day, L. A., Sturtevant, J. M., and Singer, S. J. (1963). The kinetics of the reactions between antibodies to the 2,4-dinitrophenyl group and specific haptens. Ann. N. Y. Acad. Sci. *103:* 611–625.

Eigen, M., and De Maeyer, L. (1962). Relaxation methods. In *Techniques of Organic Chemistry*, 2nd Ed., Vol. 8, A. Weissburger, ed., Interscience (New York, 1582 pp.), pp. 895–1054.

Eisen, H. N., and Karush, F. (1949). The interaction of purified antibody with homologous hapten. Antibody valence and binding constant. J. Am. Chem. Soc. *71:* 363–364.

Eisen, H. N., and Pearce, J. H. (1962). The nature of antibodies and antigens. Ann. Rev. Microbiol. *16:* 101–126.

Eisen, H. N., and Siskind, G. W. (1964). Variations in affinities of antibodies during the immune response. Biochemistry *3:* 996–1008.

Froese, A., and Sehon, A. H. (1964). Kinetics of antibody-hapten reactions. Ber. Bunsenges Physik. Chem. *68:* 863–864.

Froese, A., and Sehon, A. H. (1965). Kinetic and equilibrium studies of the reaction between anti-*p*-nitrophenyl antibodies and a homologous hapten. Immunochemistry *2:* 135–143.

Froese, A., Sehon, A. H., and Eigen, M. (1962). Kinetic studies of protein-dye and antibody-hapten interactions with the temperature-jump method. Can. J. Chem. *40:* 1786–1797.

Goebel, W. F., Avery, O. T., and Babers, F. H. (1934). Chemo-immunological studies on conjugate carbohydrate proteins. IX. The specificity of antigens prepared by combining the p-aminophenol glycosides of disaccharides with protein. J. Exptl. Med. *60:* 599–617.

Grossberg, A. L., and Pressman, D. (1960). Nature of the combining site of antibody against a hapten bearing a positive charge. J. Am. Chem. Soc. *82:* 5478–5482.

Haurowitz, F., and Breinl, F. (1933). Chemische Untersuchung der specifischen Bindung von Arsanil-Eiweiss und Arsanilsäure an Immunserum. Hoppe-Seyler's Z. Physiol. Chem. *214:* 111–120.

Kantor, F. S., Ojeda, A., and Benacerraf, B. (1963). Studies on artificial antigens. I. Antigenicity of DNP-polylysine and DNP copolymer of lysine and glutamic acid in guinea pigs. J. Exptl. Med. *117:* 55–69.

Karush, F. (1956). The interaction of purified antibody with optically isomeric hapten. J. Am. Chem. Soc. *78:* 5519–5526.

Karush, F. (1957). The interaction of purified anti-β-lactoside antibody with haptens. J. Am. Chem. Soc. *79:* 3380–3384.

Karush, F. (1958). Structural and energetic aspects of antibody-hapten interactions. Conf. Protein Metab. (Rutgers) *4:* 40–55.

Karush, F. (1962). Immunologic specificity and molecular structure. Advan. Immunol. *2:* 1–40.

Karush, F., and Sonnenberg, M. (1949). Interaction of homologous alkyl sulfates with bovine serum albumin. J. Am. Chem. Soc. *71:* 1369–1376.

Klinman, N. R., Rockey, J. H., Frauenberger, G., and Karush, F. (1966). Equine anti-hapten antibody. III. The comparative properties of γG- and γA-antibodies. J. Immunol. *96:* 587–595.

Koshland, M. E., and Englberger, F. (1963). Differences in the amino acid composition of two purified antibodies from the same rabbit. Proc. Natl. Acad. Sci. U. S. *50:* 61–68.

Landsteiner, K. (1921). Über heterogenetisches Antigen und Hapten XV. Mitteilung über Antigene. Biochem. Z. *119:* 294–306.

Landsteiner, K., and van der Scheer, J. (1928). Serological differentiation of steric isomers. J. Exptl. Med. *48:* 315–320.

Levine, B. B., Ojeda, A., and Benacerraf, B. (1963). Basis for the antigenicity of hapten-poly-L-lysine conjugates in random-bred guinea pigs. Nature *200:* 544–546.

Marrack, J., and Smith, F. C. (1932). Quantitative aspects of immunity reactions: the combination of antibodies with simple haptenes. Brit. J. Exptl. Pathol. *13:* 394–402.

Maurer, P. H., Gerulat, B. F., and Pinchuck, P. (1962). Antigenicity of polypeptides (poly alpha amino acids) VII. Studies in humans. J. Exptl. Med. *116:* 521–533.

Maurer, P. H., Subrahmanyann, D., Katchalski, E., and Blout, E. R. (1959). Antigenicity of polypeptides (poly alpha amino acids). J. Immunol. *83:* 193–197.

Nisonoff, A., and Pressman, D. (1958a). Heterogeneity and average combining constants of antibodies from individual rabbits. J. Immunol. *80:* 417–428.

Nisonoff, A., and Pressman, D. (1958b). Heterogeneity of antibody sites in their relative combining affinities for structurally related haptens. J. Immunol. *81:* 126–135.

Nisonoff, A., and Woernley, D. L. (1959). Effect of hydrolysis by papain on the combining sites of an antibody. Nature *183:* 1325–1326.

Pauling, L. (1940). A theory of the structure and process of formation of antibodies. J. Am. Chem. Soc. *62:* 2643–2657.

Scatchard, G., (1949). The attractions of proteins for small molecules and ions. Ann. N. Y. Acad. Sci. *51:* 660–672.

Schechter, I., Bauminger, S., Sela, M., Nachtigal, D., and Feldman, M. (1964). Immune response to polypeptidyl proteins in rabbits tolerant to the protein carriers. Immunochemistry *1:* 249–265.

Schneider, H., and Sehon, A. H. (1961). Determination of the lower limits for the rate constants of a hapten-antibody reaction by polarography. Trans. N. Y. Acad. Sci. *24:* 15–22.

Sehon, A. H. (1963). Kinetics of antibody-hapten interactions. Ann. N. Y. Acad. Sci. *103:* 626–629.

Singer, S. J. (1964). On the heterogeneity of anti-hapten antibodies. Immunochemistry *1:* 15–20.

Singer, S. J. (1965). Structure and function of antigen and antibody proteins. In *The Proteins*, 2nd Ed., Vol. III, H. Neurath, ed., Academic Press (New York, pp. 269–357), p. 343.

Singer, S. J., and Campbell, D. H. (1953). Physical chemical studies of soluble antigen-antibody complexes. II. Equilibrium properties. J. Am. Chem. Soc. *75:* 5577–5578.

Stahmann, M., Lapresle, C., Buchanan-Davidson, D. J., and Grabar, P. (1959). Immunochemistry of synthetic polypeptides and polypeptidyl proteins. I. Qualitative studies on the modified proteins. J. Immunol. *83:* 534–542.

Talmage, D. W. (1960). The kinetics of the reaction between antibody and bovine serum albumin using the Farr method. J. Infect. Diseases *107:* 115–132.

Velick, S. F., Parker, C. W., and Eisen, H. N. (1960). Excitation energy transfer and the quantitative study of the antibody hapten reaction. Proc. Natl. Acad. Sci. U. S. *46:* 1470–1482.

Winkler, M. A. (1964). A molecular probe for the antibody site. J. Mol. Biol. *4:* 118–120.

8
Precipitation Reactions

1. Introduction

During the formative years of biochemistry considerable interest was displayed in the precipitates that formed in natural fluids such as milk, plasma, and fruit juices. For one thing such precipitates generally represented substances of increased purity that would lend themselves more easily to analysis, and it was natural that casein, fibrin, and pectin would become the initial targets for investigation. For another, the soluble material (serum) remaining after precipitation (in the case of milk and plasma) was enriched enough in albumins that it also became readily subject to analysis.

One of the ways of purifying albumins still further was to inject the serum of milk or blood from one animal into one of another species and later to combine the serum of the immune animal with that of the original. In this way milk serum albumins (now known as lactalbumin) or blood serum albumins could also be made to precipitate. By cross-immunizations it was found that "nearly the whole quantity of the albuminous substances [in the original serum], but only a very small fraction of those [in the immune serum], enter into the precipitate" (Arrhenius, 1907). It was clear to Arrhenius and other physical chemists of the era, however, that something was different about immune precipitation. The antibody apparently was not acting as a catalyst, in the way rennet did in the formation of casein, but rather as a participant in a bimolecular reaction. The nature of the precipitation reaction, however, was so peculiar that a rational mechanism and a mathematical model were not easily derived from it. The most startling feature was the complete solubility of the precipitate in a solution of excess antigen. Although complex formations had been met in inorganic chemistry in which one of the reactants would, in excess, solubilize what it had precipitated in more dilute solution, the phenomenon had not been met before in biochemistry.

Arrhenius tabulated the data of his colleague, Hamburger, to indicate the manner in which peak precipitation would occur and derived an equation that expressed the whole process. A rabbit antiserum had been prepared against sheep serum and then tested against sheep, goat, and

TABLE 15

Precipitation of Sheep, Goat, and Bullock Sera with Rabbit Anti-Sheep Serum

Volume of Antigen		Volume Units of Precipitate Formed (P)*					
		Sheep		Goat		Bullock	
Amount	Equivalent†	Observed	Calculated	Observed	Calculated	Observed	Calculated
cc							
0.002	0.08	1	0.5	1	0.4	1	0.5
0.04	1.6	2	1.3	2	1.2	2	1.3
0.1	4	3	3.5	4	3.4	4	3.4
0.15	6	6	5.3	5	5.2	5	5.2
0.2	8	7	7.2	6	7	7	6.7
0.6	24	21	21.5	16	21	16	19
1	40	35	34	26	32	20	24
1.5	60	39	48	30	43	22	26
2	80	60	57	35	48	25	26
3	120	67	66	40	51	28	25
5	200	64	65	50	47	22	21
7	280	58	58	52	40	10	17
10	400	49	46	34	27	7	11
12	480			27	18	5	7
15	600	10	19	9	5	3	1
18	720	5	3	8	0	2	0
20	800	2	0	4	0	1	0

(From Arrhenius, 1907.)

* One volume unit of precipitate equals 0.0004 cc.

† Number of equivalents of 2% sheep serum that would optimally precipitate undiluted rabbit antiserum. Amount of antiserum was fixed at 0.4 cc, enough to precipitate 120 equivalents from 3 cc of 2% sheep serum at optimum.

bullock sera for precipitation. Varying volumes of the test antigens were added to constant volumes (0.4 cc) of rabbit antiserum in a funnel-shaped vessel which extended into a calibrated capillary tube of 0.04-cc volume, divided into units of 0.0004 cc. By vigorous hand centrifugation for 1.5–2 hours, the precipitates would pack into the capillary tubes where their volume could be measured. The data in Table 15 are given in terms of 0.0004-cc volume units of precipitate for various volumes (in cc) of added test antigen. The calculated values were obtained from equations that were remarkable in concept for that era.

A bimolecular reaction was assumed in which the soluble reactants were in equilibrium with the insoluble product according to the law of mass action. At equilibrium between the two phases the solubility product law was then utilized, expressing the product of the concentration of reactants as, K, an equilibrium constant. A was given as multiples of the number of equivalents of 2% sheep serum that would form an optimum precipitate with rabbit antiserum, and B was given as multiples of the number of equivalents of undiluted rabbit serum that would form 100 units of precipitate at optimum. In these experiments 1 ml of diluted sheep serum was found to contain 40 equivalents and 1 ml of undiluted rabbit antiserum, 300 equivalents; i.e., 2.5 ml of 2% sheep serum were equivalent to 0.33 ml of rabbit antiserum, and the two together would form a full capillary of 100 precipitin units. The precipitate, P, that was formed was assumed to be homogeneous and to contain equivalent precipitin units of both antigen and antibody such that the amounts of A and B left in solution would be $(A - P)$ and $(B - P)$. The total volume V would be the same for each and the concentrations would therefore be $(A - P)/V$ and $(B - P)/V$. Thus,

$$\left(\frac{A - P}{V}\right)\left(\frac{B - P}{V}\right) = K$$

or

$$(A - P)(B - P) = K \cdot V^2$$

Since B was kept at 0.4 cc or 120 precipitin units the final equation was

$$(A - P)(120 - P) = K \cdot V^2$$

Values for K were obtained by plotting the observed values $(A - P)$ $(120 - P)$, against V^2. In the case of sheep serum, $K = 250$; goat serum, $K = 200$; bullock serum, $K = 85$. The calculated values for P in Table 15 were obtained by assuming these K values.

Remarkable as the concept is upon which this first precipitin equation was based, it is for the most part erroneous (wherein lies an example of the danger of curve fitting to observed data). Discussion of its flaws will be instructive in understanding the precipitin reaction for what it is.

The first flaw is the assumption that the formed precipitate is homogeneous. It is not homogeneous, but rather a mixture of several components varying in the ratio of antigen to antibody and in total aggregated size. The nature of some of these antigen-antibody complexes will be discussed in a later section and their inhomogeneity will then become apparent.

The second flaw is the assumption that the number of equivalents worked out between rabbit antiserum and its homologous antigen, sheep serum, should hold for cross-reacting antigens. The same number of equivalents A were assigned to a given volume of goat or bullock serum as to sheep serum, and the number of equivalents in 0.4 ml of rabbit serum was assumed to be 120 regardless of the antigen against which it was used. Equivalence zones should have been worked out for each system.

The third flaw is the assumption that the precipitation reaction is volume-independent and requires only considerations of concentration to be valid. Actually, volumes are critical in obtaining quantitative precipitin data and must be kept constant to obtain the most meaningful and reproducible curves.

The fourth flaw is the assumption that the precipitation reaction is practically over by the time the first precipitate is observed. The attainment of a reproducible amount of precipitate takes several hours and, because it is temperature-dependent, requires application of constant temperature.

The fifth flaw is the assumption that the amount of precipitate formed is directly proportional to the amount of antigen precipitated. A variant of the first flaw, this draws attention to the necessity of analyzing the formed precipitate for its antigen and antibody content before applying the data to antigenic analysis.

The sixth flaw is the assumption that the volume of precipitate obtained after packing in a centrifuge is a precise measure of the amount of precipitate present. In protein work such a measure is one of the least precise.

The seventh and perhaps the most serious flaw is the assumption that the law of mass action can be simply applied to the precipitation reaction—to the simple interactions of free haptens and antibodies, yes, but not to the complex interactions that lead up to precipitation.

In spite of the invalid assumptions that made this first mathematical expression of the precipitin reaction erroneous, two conclusions were drawn that were valid, basic, and extremely important: that antibodies are bound to the precipitates they help form and that an equivalence zone exists where antigen and antibody form the optimum amount of precipitate.

The most appealing observations made during the early years of immunochemistry were, perhaps, those of von Dungern (1903). In retrospect they appear to have a contemporary flavor and in them is contained the prototype of the modern experiment. Rabbit antisera were prepared against octopus, crab, and mollusc plasmas and shown to react with hemocyanins to form blue-colored precipitates. (Hemocyanins are blue proteins that form the major part of many invertebrate plasma proteins. They contain no heme but do have copper-peptide prosthetic groups.) By manipulations of reactant concentrations that formed the precipitates von Dungern was able to demonstrate that, in either direction from apparent optimum, hemocyanin precipitates would change in composition. He further showed that the hemocyanins, while in the form of specific precipitates, would become colorless when exposed to CO_2 and would regain their color when exposed to air (O_2). These experiments, while not particularly quantitative, demonstrated the value of having a direct measure of antigen with which to follow the process of precipitation.

2. The quantitative precipitation of pneumococcal polysaccharides

The more than 75 types and subtypes of pneumococci (Heidelberger, 1956) receive their specificities from capsules which, under optimal conditions of growth, cover a maximum number of organisms. Loss of virulence on the part of the organisms is associated with capsular loss and also with the loss of immunological specificity.

Heidelberger and Avery (1923) demonstrated the polysaccharide nature of the solubilized specific substance from Type II pneumococcus capsules, and in a second paper (1924) reported that the polysaccharides from Types II and III organisms were chemically different. S-III was soon shown to be an aldobiuronic acid (Heidelberger and Goebel, 1927) that was nitrogen-free and that was freely soluble in salt form. That this early form of S-III was partially degraded by heat, as shown by Heidelberger, Kendall, and Scherp (1936), did not detract from its usefulness as a purified and nitrogen-free antigen in the study of the precipitation reaction with anti-S-III. The structure of S-III was confirmed by Reeves and Goebel (1941) as that of an aldobiuronic acid and was shown to have a β-D-configuration.

Repeating unit of S-III polyaldobiuronic acid

The usefulness of the S-III polysaccharide in the quantitative study of the precipitin reaction is readily apparent. As shown by Heidelberger and Kendall (1929) the difference in the original nitrogen content of the antibody solution and that remaining after precipitation and centrifugation of the specific precipitate produced an accurate measure of the amount of precipitated antibody in absolute weight units since the antigen contained no nitrogen. Increased precision was obtained by using specifically purified antibody as the starting material and thereby decreasing the amount of original nitrogen (by eliminating nitrogen-containing non-specific protein).

With the advent of more precise micro methods for determining precipitated antibody nitrogen, thus making direct nitrogen analyses of washed precipitates possible, the precipitin reaction could be investigated in depth.

Heidelberger's review (1939) sums up the application of the quantitative technique in the study of antigen-antibody reactions. When small amounts of S-III were added to a large amount of horse anti-S-III, 240 mg of antibody were precipitated per mg of S-III. When increasing amounts of S-III were added to separate portions of antibody, increasing amounts of precipitate were obtained with no discontinuity and with no antigen detectable in the soluble phase at a dilution of $1:1 \times 10^7$. Antibody was still present in the separated soluble phase since additional precipitate would form when S-III was added to it. This whole region was called the *antibody excess zone*. The *equivalence zone* was reached at the point where neither S-III nor anti-S-III was demonstrable, except perhaps in very small amount, in the soluble phase. As S-III continued to be added a point was eventually reached where antibody nitrogen in the precipitate remained at the maximum but where S-III began to appear in the supernatant fluid. This was the end of the equivalence zone and the beginning of the *first zone of antigen excess*. With a much larger excess of S-III added to antibody an *inhibition zone or second zone of antigen excess* was finally reached in which, as S-III continued to be added, less and less precipitate formed until its appearance was finally prevented. A graphical precipitin curve, recording these events, is shown in Figure 22.

When the reaction was confined to the antibody excess region where the amount of added S-III was completely precipitated, it was observed that as the amount of added S-III was increased, the amount of antibody nitrogen that was precipitated with the added S-III did not increase proportionately, i.e., that the ratio of antibody nitrogen to S-III in the formed precipitate did not remain constant (Heidelberger and Kendall, 1935a).

An empirical relationship was worked out, nevertheless, since it was observed that plotting the ratio of antibody nitrogen to added S-III against added S-III resulted in a linear relationship (keeping in mind that added S-III was also precipitated S-III). Thus,

$$\frac{\text{pptd Ab N}}{\text{added S-III}} = a - b \text{ (added S-III)}$$

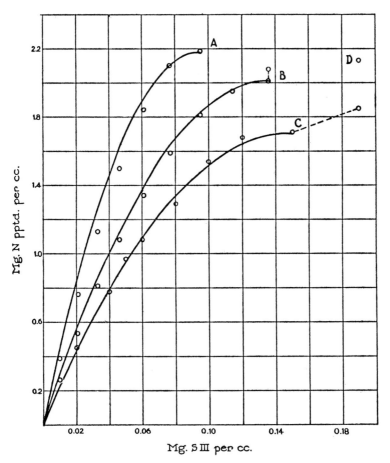

FIG. 22. Precipitation titration of anti-S-III by additions of S-III. Curve C, standard method at 37°C; curves A and B, serial additions of S-III in small amounts at 0°C and 37°C, respectively. The higher values obtained with B than with C demonstrate the Danysz phenomenon. The higher values obtained with A than with B demonstrate the temperature effect. (Heidelberger and Kendall, 1935a.)

$$\frac{\text{pptd Ab N}}{\text{pptd S-III}} = a - b \text{ (added S-III)}$$

where conditions are confined to antibody excess regions and all added antigen is also precipitated antigen (Fig. 23).

The constants can be evaluated by considering the ratio R for the two

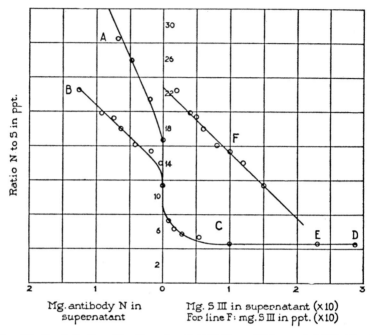

FIG. 23. Precipitation titration of anti-S-III by additions of S-III. The line *F* is the pertinent one for the text discussion. Note that the abscissa for *F* is milligrams of S-III in precipitate, which is also milligrams of added S-III since the titration was carried out in antibody excess. Curves *A* and *B* also represent antibody excess; curve *C*, antigen excess. Curve *A* to point *E* is for antibody B-62 at 0°C. Curve *B* to point *D* is for antibody B-61 at 37°C. Point *D* should read 3.68. (Heidelberger and Kendall, 1935b.)

components at equivalence (usually the mid-point):

$$R \equiv \left(\frac{\text{pptd Ab N}}{\text{pptd S-III}}\right)_{\text{equiv}}$$

First, it will be noted that the intercept a on the ordinate is double the value obtained within the equivalence zone; i.e., $a = 2R$. Thus,

$$\underset{\substack{\text{added S-III} \\ \to 0}}{\text{limit}} \left(\frac{\text{pptd Ab N}}{\text{pptd S-III}}\right) = a = 2R$$

and

$$\underset{\substack{\text{added S-III} \\ \to \text{equiv}}}{\text{limit}} \left(\frac{\text{pptd Ab N}}{\text{pptd S-III}}\right) = R$$

Therefore, at equivalence,

$$R = 2R - b \text{ (added S-III)}_{\text{equiv}}$$

and

$$b = R/(\text{added S-III})_{\text{equiv}}$$

Since

$$(\text{added S-III})_{\text{equiv}} = (\text{pptd S-III})_{\text{equiv}}$$

and

$$(\text{pptd S-III})_{\text{equiv}} = (\text{pptd Ab N})_{\text{equiv}}/R$$

letting

$$A = (\text{pptd Ab N})_{\text{equiv}}$$

$$b = R^2/A$$

The completed formula can then be written as

$$\frac{\text{pptd Ab N}}{\text{added S-III}} = 2R - \frac{R^2}{A} \text{ (added S-III)}$$

$$\frac{N}{S} = 2R - \frac{R^2}{A} S$$

It was of interest to evaluate the precipitin reactions of antibodies obtained from rabbit anti-S-III in order to see if the empirical relationships would still hold. As an extension of the study it was also of interest to note any changes in precipitin response as the rabbits were immunized by repeated injections (Heidelberger and Kendall, 1937). An initial course of 15 injections were administered over a period of 4–5 weeks to two rabbits, 3–4 injections per week, with dosages increasing from 1 ml to 3 ml containing 0.05 mg of bacterial N/ml. The first bleeding occurred 4 days after the last injection in the first course; the second, after a week's rest, a course of 12 injections, and another week's rest; the third bleeding, similar to the second; and the fourth, likewise.

The first observation was that the data for precipitation of rabbit anti-S-III with S-III were linear when plotted in the same manner as horse anti-S-III. The second observation was that the value R increased during immunization. The third was that the value R was different for each rabbit at a given stage of immunization as it had been for individual horse antibody preparations (Table 16).

When it is recalled that R equals the ratio of antibody nitrogen to S-III at the mid-point of equivalence it can easily be understood that there is no set stoichiometric formula expressing equivalence such that

TABLE 16

Precipitation Equation of S-III with Various Antisera

Species	Antiserum No.	Equation
Horse	BVA	$N/S = 27.2 - 45.6S$
	B36	$N/S = 24.8 - 82.7S$
	B61	$N/S = 22.8 - 76.0S$
Rabbit	3.51—1st bleeding	$N/S = 12.7 - 40.3S$
	2nd	$N/S = 14.5 - 52.6S$
	3rd	$N/S = 16.1 - 64.8S$
	4th	$N/S = 16.7 - 69.7S$
	3.50—1st bleeding	$N/S = 14.9 - 46.2S$
	2nd	$N/S = 15.6 - 60.8S$
	3rd	$N/S = 16.8 - 70.6S$

(From Heidelberger and Kendall, 1937.)

all antisera could be equated at that point. This is not surprising in view of what has already been said about heterogeneity, but it has complicated theoretical treatment of the reaction almost beyond experimental verification. Two general assumptions of Heidelberger and Kendall (1935b) and of Marrack (1938) still stand in spite of controversy over a number of other points: (1) Multivalency of antigen and antibody were assumed (and there is no longer any doubt about this assumption); (2) the behavior of the antibody mixture was taken as that of a single substance on the average. (The precision of the equation could not be expected without this being true.)

Before precipitation occurred a number of bimolecular reactions were assumed to take place with the rate of formation of reaction products being proportional to the concentration of reacting substances. This seemed to be the only way of explaining why discrete steps in composition were not found in going from one end of the antibody excess region to the other. *The composition of the precipitate would depend more on the proportions in which the components were mixed than upon the antibody concentration at equilibrium or at the end of the reaction.* There were many objections to this idea, most of them following Marrack (1938), in questioning the apparent irreversibility that would be necessary to "fix" the compositions of soluble reaction products before they formed aggregates.

Heidelberger's answer to this objection was to perform another experiment (Heidelberger, Treffers, and Mayer, 1940). It had already been established that the general form of the precipitin equation would hold for rabbit anti-egg albumin (anti-EA) in its reaction with EA. On the other hand, it was also known that a sample of Pappenheimer's horse anti-EA was "incomplete," that it would bind but not precipitate EA. The experiment that could be performed with the horse and rabbit anti-EA antisera was to find out how long it would take for horse anti-EA (H) to form a soluble complex with EA, then to dissociate reversibly, and finally to make EA available for precipitation with added rabbit anti-EA (R). It was found that if R were added to H-EA as little as 18 sec after H and EA were mixed, only 0.02 mg of nitrogen precipitated out of a total of 0.18 mg in 1 day. Not until after 2–3 weeks did the reverse reaction of H-EA dissociation complete itself and make EA available for precipitation with R. When 3:1 R and H were mixed and then added to EA, 0.12 mg out of 0.18 mg of total available nitrogen was precipitated, showing that the velocities of initial reactions of R and H were comparable. When R was added immediately before H, complex formation of R-EA was complete and precipitation maximal. *Thus, it was demonstrated that the concentration of initial reactants and the rate of formation of soluble reaction products did indeed affect the nature of the precipitate and that equilibrium processes involved in precipitation were much slower.*[1]

This does not prove conclusively that Heidelberger and Kendall (1935b) were right in their theory, but it does mean that the objections to their theory were certainly not the right ones. Heidelberger (1939), himself, felt that

> ... this oversimplification of the quantitative theory as it now stands ... at least permits many calculations and predictions to be made with accuracy and a certain degree of utility. ... The theory was offered, in the realization of many weaknesses, as a temporary expedient which might be useful until antibody possessed of uniform reactivity could be isolated.

The *empirical precipitation equation* has suffered unduly because of the unrest concerning its meaning. Although it can be derived from the

---

[1] It is enlightening to compare the results obtained by Heidelberger, Treffers, and Mayer (1940) with those recent ones of Klinman, Rockey, Frauenberger, and Karush (1966). The latter group followed the development of anti-Lac-HSA in a single horse with respect to distribution of antibody activity among six different immunoglobulins, and found that early serum, high in precipitable IgG, precipitated Lac-HSA. However, as IgA became the major component in later serum, no precipitation of Lac-HSA occurred. When IgG in the late serum was separated and tested, it was capable of precipitating the conjugated Lac-protein. Changes in the precipitability of serum in the horse were thus easily attributed to the relative competition between mixtures of precipitable bivalent IgG and non-precipitable *bivalent* IgA, a conclusion drawn likewise by Heidelberger, Treffers, and Mayer (1940) for a very similar system.

Heidelberger-Kendall theory, *it does not depend upon that theory for its validity.* Unlike the Arrhenius equation, no assumptions were necessary to formulate this one, and no attempt was made to cover all regions with one formula.

Other empirical formulas were found on occasion to provide better linearity. One of these was worked out for a protein-antiprotein system in which the test antigen was coupled to a colored dye (Heidelberger and Kendall, 1935c). Total precipitated nitrogen was determined directly, antigen nitrogen was determined by its known ratio to the colorimetric amount of antigen present, and antibody nitrogen was obtained by difference. The equation was

$$N = 3RD - 2\sqrt{\frac{R^3 D^3}{A}}$$

where R = ratio of N to D at equivalence, i.e., $A{:}D$
$\quad N$ = antibody nitrogen
$\quad D$ = dye-antigen nitrogen
$\quad A$ = maximum precipitable antibody nitrogen
A more familiar form and one used for demonstrating linearity is

$$\frac{N}{D} = 3R - 2\sqrt{\frac{R^3}{A}}\,\sqrt{D}$$

where N/D is plotted against the square root of added antigen nitrogen or $\sqrt{D}$. This was the form used by Kabat and Berg (1953) to describe the precipitin reactions of human anti-dextran antibodies with a number of native and clinical dextrans (Table 17).

TABLE 17

Empirical Precipitin Equations for Dextran-Anti-Dextran Systems

Dextran	Antiserum	Equation
Native (B742)*	1-D-2	$N/D = 0.87 - 0.06D^{\frac{1}{2}}$
	20-D-2	$N/D = 0.92 - 0.05D^{\frac{1}{2}}$
	30-D-2	$N/D = 0.79 - 0.04D^{\frac{1}{2}}$
	49-D-2	$N/D = 0.63 - 0.03D^{\frac{1}{2}}$
Clinical	1-D-2	$N/D = 12.1 - 3.1D^{\frac{1}{2}}$
(N150N)†	20-D-2	$N/D = 12.8 - 2.8D^{\frac{1}{2}}$
	30-D-2	$N/D = 11.9 - 2.5D^{\frac{1}{2}}$
	49-D-2	$N/D = 11.7 - 3.0D^{\frac{1}{2}}$

(From Kabat and Berg, 1953.)
* The ratio of 1,6 to non-1,6 links in dextran was 1.9.
† The ratio of 1,6 to non-1,6 links in dextran was 32–49.

An example of the power inherent in the intelligent use of the quantitative precipitin reaction is found in a procedure for antibody purification that was predicted on the basis of the reaction. Heidelberger, Kendall, and Teorell (1936) had noted the following:

1.24 mg of horse anti-S-III Ab N pptd by 0.1 mg of S-III in 0.15 м NaCl

1.01 mg of horse anti-S-III Ab N pptd by 0.1 mg of S-III in 1.75 м NaCl

It seemed to Heidelberger and Kendall (1936) that if the reaction were carried out in 0.15 м NaCl and the precipitate were collected and washed, and if then the precipitate were agitated in 1.75 м NaCl, then 0.23 mg of nitrogen should dissociate in the form of antibody. If this indeed were true, then salt dissociation should form the basis of a purification procedure for anti-S-III antibody. The technique was tried and the predicted amount of antibody in 90–98 % purity was obtained in a number of trials.

It was this simple procedure that led to the finding that horse, cow, and pig antipneumococcal polysaccharide antibodies were IgM whereas those from rabbit, monkey, and man were IgG (Heidelberger and Pedersen, 1937; Tiselius and Kabat, 1938; Kabat, 1939; Tiselius and Kabat, 1939).

The immunological specificity of pneumococcal polysaccharides and the cross-reactions displayed among them has been the main subject of study by Heidelberger and his colleagues, and the development of quantitative techniques for antigenic analysis was pursued to make detailed exploration possible. One of the many problems solved by application of quantitative technique concerned an atypical Type III pneumococcus isolated by Sugg, Gaspari, Fleming, and Neill (1928). The work of Cooper, Edwards, and Rosenstein (1929) had shown that the atypical strain cross-reacted with anti-S-III but failed to remove all anti-S-III activity. The new form was then called Type VIII, and Goebel (1935) confirmed the nature of its difference from Type III. Though its polysaccharide contained the same aldobiuronic acid as S-III, there was a glucose in addition. It was not until 1957 that Jones and Perry tentatively worked out the fine structure of S-VIII as containing a repeating unit of

[-4-β-D-glucuronic-(1 $\rightarrow$ 4)-β-D-glucose-(1 $\rightarrow$ 4)-

α-D-glucose-(1 $\rightarrow$ 4)-α-D-galactose-(1 $\rightarrow$)]

In a cross-reaction study Heidelberger, Kabat, and Shrivastava (1937) showed that although a horse anti-S-III reagent contained 30 % cross-reacting antibody that would react with S-VIII, a rabbit anti-S-III con-

tained little or no cross-reacting antibody even though it would react in
very high titer with S-III. The subtle differences in structures between
the two cellobiuronic acids were enough to make it not always possible to
protect individuals against both pneumococcal types by immunization
with only one. In spite of this both types of antisera in high dilution were
found to precipitate the soluble sodium salts of oxidized cotton cellulose
(Heidelberger and Hobby, 1942), indicating that the latter contained
cellobiuronic acid residues.

As reagents for identifying specific polysaccharide groupings from a
number of other sources, the antipneumococcal polysaccharides have
been extremely invaluable. The hydrolyzed polysaccharide from the
slime of *Sphaerotilus natans* was found to form precipitates, e.g., with
anti-S-III and anti-S-VIII, showing the presence of the cellobiuronic
acid, β-D-glucuronopyranosyl-(1 $\rightarrow$ 4)-D-glucose (Heidelberger, Gaudy,
and Wolfe, 1964). Chemical modification of S-III by complete acetylation, which esterified the carboxyl groups, was found to destroy its
binding capacity for anti-S-III, but when progressive deacetylation was
carried out reactivity was regained until, with all acetyl groups removed,
the material reacted with anti-S-III as well as it had before acetylation.
It was of interest, however, that esterification of 35 % of the carboxyl
groups and conversion to the amide gave a product 86–90 % as reactive
as the native material. It was understandable from these results why
anti-S-III reacted so well with oxidized cotton cellulose—the latter contained 16–21 % carboxylic acid groups.

The cyclic process of investigations involving the pneumococcal polysaccharide systems still continues—cyclic in the sense that as new structures are found, they eventually become identified and purified, and in
turn help to characterize the very antiserum reagents that led to their
identification. These lead back to methods for preparing pneumococcal
polysaccharides in a less degraded and more complete state and permit
more extended and detailed cross-reaction studies among the various
types. The end result is new knowledge about the structures and specific
groupings of polysaccharides in general. Sometimes this can lead to the
elucidation of a repeating unit as in the case of S-VI, in which O-α-D-
galactopyranosyl - (1$\rightarrow$3) - O-D-glucopyranosyl - (1$\rightarrow$3) - O-α-L-rhamno-
pyranosyl - (1$\rightarrow$3) - D (or L) - ribitol was obtained (Rebers and Heidelberger, 1961). It was found that the adjacent units in the undegraded
polysaccharide were joined together by phosphate diester linkages in
head-to-tail fashion and that type specificity came in three parts (Heidelberger and Rebers, 1960): linear chains of (1 $\rightarrow$ 3)-linked L-rhamnose,
(1$\rightarrow$3) - linked D-glucose, and (1$\rightarrow$2) - linked D-galactose. The cross-

reaction of anti-S-VI with polysaccharide prepared from Group A hemolytic streptococci (known to contain L-rhamnose) suggested that the Group A sugar might also contain $(1 \rightarrow 3)$-linked rhamnose residues, and this was confirmed by chemical studies (Heymann, Manniello, and Barkulis, 1963).

The quantitative precipitin reaction need not be confined to polysaccharides and proteins but can be extended to the agglutination of bacteria and other particulate materials. Heidelberger and Kabat (1937) demonstrated this in the case of horse anti-S-I in its precipitation of Type I pneumococcus. Several controls were of course necessary. (One serious problem was to control for the amount of S-I that tended to leach out from the organism and form precipitates independent of the bacteria.) A technique was finally worked out, using purified antibody, that provided reproducible data and, most important, that gave rise to linearity when the precipitin equation was used. In the region of antibody excess the bacteria were found to agglutinate easily and to resuspend uniformly. A temperature difference was found such that the equations were, in 0.15 M NaCl,

$$N/S = 8.0 - 26.9S \text{ at } 37°C$$

and

$$N/S = 5.7 - 11.6S \text{ at } 0°C$$

The increased value of R (4.0 vs. 2.85) at the higher temperature (increased amount of antibody bound per cell) was explained as a mechanical difference in which more surface S-I was present at 37°C than at 0°C. In terms of the amount of S-I present in the bacteria (which would have precipitated anti-S-I if in the freely soluble form), less than a maximum number of bacteria were precipitated per equivalent amount of antibody. This was quite reasonably taken to indicate that not all S-I was available in reactive form at the cell surface.

In the same way that the dissociation of specific precipitates was predicted to and did take place in strong salt, dissociation of specific agglutinates was similarly found to occur (Heidelberger and Kabat, 1938).

3. Precipitation and solubilization in antigen-excess regions

Although the most useful regions for quantitative immunochemical determinations have been those expressive of antibody excess and of equivalence, the region of antigen excess has provided an area for some of the more revealing studies on the nature of antigen-antibody interaction. Marrack's (1938) description of what probably happens is still more or less acceptable today:

> ... no precipitation will occur in the post-zone (antigen excess) owing to the formation of small aggregates ... protected by the excess of antigen. With smaller quantities of antigen continuously larger aggregates will be formed, possibly arranged as a lattice with incomplete packing of the antibody molecules. These may settle, leaving the supernatant fluid cloudy, owing to the presence in it of large aggregates. At optimum proportions a continuous lattice will be formed.

Marrack regarded the optimum proportion to be that ratio of antibody to antigen which is capable of forming a stable lattice, and by this view, but for different reasons, was in accord with Taylor (1931) and with Burnet (1931). A stable lattice

> ... will be determined partly by a question of size. In the instance in which the antigen, serum globulin, is of approximately the same size as the antibody the ratio is 1 to 4. This would be given by a lattice ... with each antigen molecule surrounded by 16 antibody molecules and each antibody molecule by 4 antigen molecules.

How a stable lattice is achieved with bivalent antibody and multivalent antigen is still unknown since the number of possibilites is large; however, the essential correctness of Marrack's framework theory for the final product is supported by much evidence. [One of the latest pictures (Fig. 24), revealed through electron microscopy, indicates that insoluble complexes may be linked through two, rather than one, antibody molecules (Feinstein and Rowe, 1965). If this is found to be generally true, then modification of the single chain (–Ag–Ab–Ag–Ab) picture for cross-linkages *in any given direction* will have to be made.] The problem will be, in any given general solution, to account for the wide variety of antigens that vary not only in size but also in valency per unit area of surface, and to account for the different types of immunoglobulins each with heterogeneity of binding.

In the area of antigen excess the problem is made simpler since complex formation itself is simpler. Early work with systems in antigen excess was hampered, however, by the lack of physical instrumentation with which to exploit the soluble phases. Immunochemistry had been essentially an exploitation of precipitating systems since separations, so necessary to analysis, could easily be achieved. With the advent of ultracentrifugation and electrophoresis, however, the soluble phases could be explored in depth. Heidelberger and Pedersen (1937) demonstrated that several species of complexes apparently could exist in solution, and later work confirmed this. One of the most basic and detailed confirmatory studies was that of Singer and Campbell (1951, 1952).

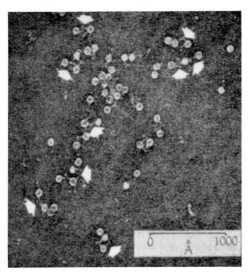

Fig. 24. Electron micrograph of ferritin-anti-ferritin complexes near equivalence, showing cross-linking strands between ferritin molecules suggestive of Ag–(Ab)₂–Ag–(Ab)₂– chains. (Feinstein and Rowe, 1965.)

Crystalline bovine serum albumin (BSA) was used as antigen, and rabbit IgG anti-BSA as antibody. In order to determine the relative amounts of BSA and anti-BSA in any given complex, the BSA was iodinated with an average of 5 atoms of iodine per antibody molecule. Thus, analysis of a given complex for total nitrogen and iodine would provide data for calculating BSA and anti-BSA. Before proceeding with analyses of complexes it was necessary to determine the effect of iodination upon BSA-anti-BSA interaction, there being essentially none for the particular antibody in the study. The procedure that was used in the main study included the following steps:

1. IgG purified by precipitation with one-third saturated ammonium sulfate.

2. Specific BSA-anti-BSA precipitates formed in equivalence zone with BSA-5I and washed with cold saline.

3. Washed (BSA-5I)-anti-BSA redissolved in antigen excess.

4. Solution of the complex brought to half saturated ammonium sulfate to form a precipitate, with unbound albumin remaining in solution. (This is the basis of the Farr technique that was developed in 1958.)

5. Precipitate suspended in buffered saline *where it completely redissolves.*

6. Solution analyzed for iodine and nitrogen to give total antigen and antibody content.

7. Solutions of greater antigen excess prepared by adding known amounts of BSA-5I to solution from Step 6.

8. Ultracentrifugation carried out in phosphate, pH 7.6, $\mu = 0.1$, and 21°C.

9. Electrophoresis carried out in Veronal, pH 8.5, $\mu = 0.1$.

Several species of antigen-antibody complexes as well as free antigen were separated by sedimentation in the ultracentrifugal field but as antigen excess increased the faster sedimenting complexes disappeared considerably until in high antigen excess only one prominent peak was obtained—the a complex. Electrophoretic resolution was poor, but a separate fast-moving peak was obtained agreeing in composition with the a complex. The question at the time was concerned with the ratio of antigen to antibody in the a complex and the valency of the antibody. From certain assumptions the composition of the a complex was taken as $(Ag)_2Ab$ and that of another, the b complex, as $(Ag)_3(Ab)_2$. As the complexes became faster sedimenting (i.e., as their molecular weight increased) their relative antigen content continually decreased until precipitation finally occurred.

The question now is no longer one of valency since that has been answered from a completely independent series of experiments (cf. the chapter on valency). The composition of the complexes as determined by Singer and Campbell (1952) can be taken as completely valid. *The question now concerns the rôle of equilibrium processes in determining the composition of the final precipitate including that at optimal proportions.* Singer and Campbell (1953) observed that the various components in antigen excess must not be in a very rapidly adjusted equilibrium. Otherwise, no resolution into separate peaks in the ultracentrifuge would have resulted. Re-equilibration due to ultracentrifugal or electrophoretic fields, however, may have prevented determination of the exact distribution of the various species in the original equilibrium mixture, as Singer and Campbell pointed out.

The modern view of the nature of soluble complexes that go on to form turbid aggregates and finally stable precipitates would hold that since the forward reaction between antibody and antigen (hapten) is generally so much more rapid than the reverse reaction, build-up of soluble complexes would be expected. Aggregation, although less rapid than dissociation of soluble complexes, would therefore begin to take place. The dissociation of aggregates *into soluble complexes* would be less rapid than their formation so that eventually aggregate build-up would occur. Finally, binding and precipitation of aggregates would take place.

In such a complex series of steps, an over-all equilibrium would not be expected until precipitation had ceased, but even then readjustments in composition of the various precipitated components would be expected to occur before the most stable form of precipitate was reached and thermodynamic equilibrium was thereby established. It is clear that until intensive physico-chemical measurements are made through the intelligent application of phase rule and phase diagrams, the nature of precipitate composition must remain in obscurity.

By 1955 Singer and Campbell had evaluated a number of homogeneous solutions of antigen-antibody complexes. Through use of the electrophoretic technique by which free antigen could be measured, there was no longer a need for the iodinated antigens; both BSA and egg albumin (EA), because of their greater mobility and distinct separation from the complexes, could be easily determined. The difference between added BSA (or EA) and free BSA (or EA) gave the value for bound antigen. Assuming that all antibody was complexed, the ratio r of bound antigen molecules to bound antibody molecules could be determined.

The data were plotted in two ways: r vs. percentage of total antigen that was free, in the 1955 papers (Singer and Campbell, 1955a, 1955b); and $1/r$ vs. $1/[Ag]$, in Singer (1957, 1965). [Ag] was the concentration of free antigen divided by the concentration of total antigen; $1/[Ag]$ was therefore a reciprocal of the percentage. In the first plot, extrapolation to 100 % free antigen (i.e., infinite antigen excess) gave r as 2, the valence of antibody. In the second plot (Fig. 25) extrapolation to the point where $1/[Ag]$ equaled unity, i.e., where all antigen was again free, gave a value for $1/r$ of 0.5 and again a value of 2 for the valence of antibody. (In the 1955 plot the curve was also completed in the other direction to 0 % free antigen, but an error in extrapolation was made since the ratio r of bound antigen to bound antibody was assumed to be 0 at 0 % free antigen. At the point where there is no longer free antigen, the equivalence zone is entered, the ratio of bound antigen to bound antibody becomes that at the edge of the equivalence zone, and a value considerably greater than zero is obtained.)

4. The Goldberg equation

Goldberg (1952) developed a theory and an equation to unify the precipitation reaction from far antibody excess to far antigen excess. The derivation is considerably complex and there is not space here to set it down. Essentially, however, it is a distribution formula which takes into account at any point in composition the number of every kind of

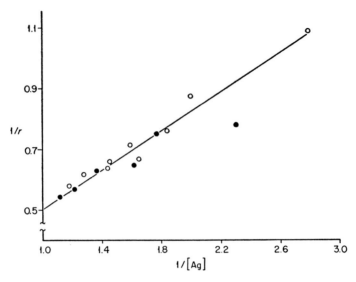

Fɪɢ. 25. Soluble complexes of bovine serum albumin (○) and egg albumin (●) with their respective antibodies in antigen excess. The parameter r is the number of moles of antigen bound per mole of antibody; $[Ag]$ is the concentration of free antigen divided by the concentration of total antigen in the solution. (Singer, 1957.)

antigen-antibody combination as well as free antigen and/or free antibody. It requires knowledge of valence of antigen, the extent of the reaction, and composition of the total mixture.

m_{ik} = number of aggregates composed of i bivalent antibody and k f-valent antigen

fG = number of antigen sites (valence) per antigen times number of antigen molecules in system

$2A$ = number of antibody sites in whole system

fk = number of antigen sites in an aggregate

q = number of free antibody sites in an aggregate

p = fraction of antigen sites in system (fG) that have reacted (also called extent of reaction)

r = $fG/2A$ = ratio of antigen sites to antibody sites in system

The distribution is written in simplified form without including univalent antibody (which is now unnecessary) and is the form used by Singer and Campbell (1953):

$$m_{ik} = fG \frac{(fk - k)!}{(fk - 2k + 2 - q)k!\, q!}\, r^{k-1} p^{k+i-1} (1-p)^{fk-k-i+1} (1-pr)^{i-k+1}$$

The Heidelberger-Kendall precipitin equation (cf. section 2) was re-written in terms of molarity and used the concept that $2R$ (where the ratio of antibody to antigen was at infinite antibody excess) was the effective antigen valence. Just as in infinite antigen excess antibody would be bound by antigen according to its valence (as shown by Singer and Campbell) so in infinite antibody excess antigen would be bound by antibody according to antigen valence, antibody reacting as if univalent. Therefore, since

$$2R = f$$

and

$$R^2/A = f^2/4A$$

it follows from the Heidelberger-Kendall equation that

$$A/G = f - f^2G/4A$$

The data from a number of papers in the literature that had been taken from experiments by Heidelberger and Kendall (1935d), Kabat and Heidelberger (1937), and Pappenheimer (1940) were converted to a mole to mole basis for antibody and antigen, and compared with calculated data from the Goldberg equation. (It can be seen that R, the ratio of bound antibody to bound antigen, is given by i/k, the number of aggregated bivalent antibodies over the number of aggregated f-valent antigens.) Two sets of data could be obtained from the Goldberg equation: maximal and critical ratios, i.e., those for the maximum extent of reaction (p_{max}) and those below which precipitation does not occur (p_c). The data for EA-anti-EA (a Heidelberger-Kendall experiment) that were considered by Goldberg (typical of several such experiments in the paper) are shown in Table 18. The agreement between the experimentally determined values, R, and the theoretical values, i/k, is remarkable. One must remember, however, that remarkable agreement between observed and calculated values were also obtained by Arrhenius (1907) even though his theoretical concept proved to be erroneous. Remarkable disagreement may disprove a theory, but remarkable agreement does not by the same token prove it.

It is natural that such a sweeping theory of the precipitation reaction, based on the distribution equation, should have its champions and its critics. All would agree, no doubt, that it does give a semiquantitative expression of the over-all precipitation reaction and the soluble aggregate formation, in spite of its drawbacks and shortcomings, and that it gives credence to Marrack's (1938) framework theory. Criticism centers mainly on the inability of the theory, based as it is upon homogeneous

TABLE 18

Theoretical and Experimental Values of Precipitate Ratios for EA-Rabbit Anti-EA

Experimental		Theoretical	
A/G	R	$(i/k)_{\max}$	$(i/k)_c$
21	3.9	4.0	
13	3.5	4.0	
7.6	3.3	4.0	3.5
4.8	2.9	4.0	2.8
3.8	2.7	3.7	2.5
2.9	2.4	2.6	2.2
2.6	2.3	2.3	2.0
2.3	2.1	2.1	1.9

(From Goldberg, 1952.)

equilibria, to describe adequately and accurately phenomena that are based upon a two-phase system (minimally). In the antigen excess region *where a single phase system* of homogeneous complexes in equilibrium can be established, the Goldberg equation has proven to be a powerful tool. Out of it has come an equation for calculating the intrinsic equilibrium constant between antigen and antibody that has proven extremely reliable (Singer, 1965, p. 307):

$$K_i = \frac{pM_A}{2C_A(1 - p)\left(1 - p\dfrac{fC_GM_A}{2C_AM_G}\right)}$$

where K_i = intrinsic equilibrium constant in M^{-1}
p = fraction of antigen sites that have reacted
C_G = concentration of antigen in grams/liter
C_A = concentration of antibody in grams/liter
M_A = molecular weight of antibody
M_G = molecular weight of antigen
f = valency of antigen
2 = valency of antibody

5. The law of equivalence

The law of equivalence states that the composition of an antigen-antibody complex is the same as the composition of the whole mixture from which it was formed. The easiest way to achieve such an end would be to precipitate all that is added—both antigen and antibody—and, indeed, this is the immunochemist's definition of an ideal equivalence

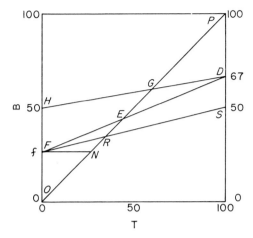

Fig. 26. Phase diagram of some ideal antigen-antibody reaction systems. The abscissa T is the mole fraction of antigen added, expressed as percent. The mole fraction of added antibody is $(100 - T)$ percent. The ordinate B is the mole fraction of bound antigen, also expressed as percent. The mole fraction of bound antibody is $(100 - B)$ percent. The line of equivalence if OP. Other lines are described in the text.

zone with the supernatant fluid free of both antigen and antibody. The law is very obvious, and one might wonder why it need be given so much attention; however, as will be made clear shortly, proper development of the theory behind quantitative immunochemistry begins with a proper understanding of the law of equivalence.

One way of illustrating equivalence is to represent it graphically as in Figure 26. The composition of the added ingredients is given in the abscissa in terms of the mole fraction of antigen T, expressed as percent. The mole fraction of added antibody is $(100 - T)$ %. The composition of the ingredients as they appear in complexed or bound form is given in the ordinate in terms of the mole fraction of bound antigen B, also expressed as percent. The mole fraction of bound antibody is $(100 - B)$ %. The line of equivalence is merely the 45° line (OP) drawn from B and T at 0 to B and T at 100.

Ideal antigen-antibody reaction systems can be described using the type of plot given in Figure 26. The effective valence of antigen at infinite antibody excess can be calculated from the intercept on the ordinate at $T = 0$. The valence is simply $(100 - B)/B$ or $(100/B) - 1$. For example, if $B = 20$, the valence, f would be 4. The valence of antibody is taken in this discussion as 2, and appears on the ordinate, when $T = 100$, as $B = 66.7$. At $T = 100$ the system of course is in infinite antigen excess. The ideal titration of an antigen-antibody system begins at $B = F$, when $T = 0$, and ends at $B = 66.7$, when $T = 100$. Theoretically, according to the present hypothesis that is being developed, *there is only one point of equivalence*, the point E where the line of titration FED intersects the line of equivalence. *When two points of equivalence are obtained and a zone of equivalence of changing composition is established between them* (and one will remember Heidelberger's description of actual zones of equivalence as characterized by changing composition), as between E and G, *a change in phase is clearly indicated*. As a matter of fact, one will recognize the present type of plot as one best suited for describing changes in product phase under the influence of a change in composition of reactants. Homogeneity of reaction is characterized in a phase diagram as a single straight line connecting an ordinate value at $T = 0$ with an ordinate value at $T = 100$.

The single line DGH drawn from $B = 66.7$ at $T = 100$ to $B = 50$ at $T = 0$ would represent binding of haptens and other univalent antigens with bivalent antibody. At infinite antigen excess one antibody would bind two haptens and at infinite antibody excess one hapten would bind one antibody. Hapten excess would be DG and antibody excess would be GH. If hapten were not completely bound in antibody excess and if antibody were not completely bound in hapten excess, an S-shaped curve would result with the curve from H arriving at equivalence below G, and not entering antigen excess until above G. The curve would be confined to the 50–66.7 % limits as long as bivalent antibody and univalent hapten were being studied.

By the same token the single line FRS drawn from $B = F$ at $T = 0$ to $B = 50$ at $T = 100$ would represent binding of univalent antibody fragments and univalent antibody hybrids with f-valent antigen. At infinite antibody excess one antigen would bind f univalent antibody fragments or hybrids; at infinite antigen excess one antibody site would bind one f-valent antigen regardless of the latter's valency. The same considerations for incomplete binding under equilibrium conditions would hold here as with haptens—an S-shaped curve would result with limits set between the ordinate values of F and 50 % (S). Phase rule would hold that such non-ideal systems would be undergoing a change in phase at equivalence resulting in an equivalence zone.

One other line requires consideration, FN, the horizontal line with the equation $B = F$. The supposition has been tacitly made either that the ingredients at any value T are mixed together all at once or that if one ingredient is added slowly to all of the others, rapid equilibrium will produce the effect of having added it all at once. If, however, binding is rapid and dissociation very slow, and if antigen is added in small amounts and slowly enough so that binding of one amount will occur before addition of the next, f-valent antigen will bind its full complement of antibody. If binding is complete and the additions are made in infinitesimally small increments, the mole percent of bound antigen will remain at F for all values of T up to equivalence and the line FN will result. This is the basis of the well-known Danysz (1902) phenomenon in which antigen (toxin) is completely neutralized by antibody (antitoxin) if added all at once to it, but, if added slowly in small increments *to the same amount of antibody*, is found as unneutralized toxin at the end of the addition. The reason is obvious. Suppose the antigen valence is 4 and the antibody valence 2; then $B = 20\%$ at $T = 0\%$ and 66.7% at $T = 100\%$.

$$B = mT + b$$

$$\therefore B = 20 = b \text{ at } T = 0$$

and

$$B = 66.7 = 100m + 20 \text{ at } T = 100$$

$$m = 0.467$$

$$\therefore B = 0.467\, T + 20$$

At equivalence,

$$B = T$$

$$\therefore 0.533T = 20$$

$$\therefore B = T = 37.5\%$$

The ratio of antibody to antigen at equivalence is, therefore, 1.8. Therefore, 180 moles of antibody will neutralize 100 moles of antigen. But 180 moles of antibody can react fully with only 180/4 or 45 moles of antigen if antigen is added in small enough increments so as to react completely at its full effective valence of 4. There will then be 55 moles of antigen added subsequently that will remain unneutralized unless and until equilibrium conditions can slowly be established.

With these simple explanations of the law of equivalence and the phase diagram that accompanies it having been made, actual data from the literature can now be considered as they appear in recalculated form in phase diagrams.

The data of Heidelberger and Kendall (1935d) for the precipitin reaction between egg albumin (EA) and rabbit anti-EA were used by

TABLE 19

Fractional Molar Composition of EA-Anti-EA Aggregates as Compared with That of the Total Mixtures of EA and Anti-EA

Source of Recalculated Data	Type of Aggregate	Mole Fraction of EA × 100		Comment on Reaction
		Total mixture	Aggregate	
		T	B	
Heidelberger and Kendall (1935d)	Precipitate	4.3	18.6	Excess Ab
	Precipitate	7.1	20.7	Excess Ab
	Precipitate	11.1	21.3	Excess Ab
	Precipitate	16.8	23.8	Excess Ab
	Precipitate	20.2	24.6	Excess Ab
	Precipitate	24.8	26.9	Excess Ab
	Precipitate	27.3	28.1	Equivalence
	Maximum precipitate	29.3	29.5	Equivalence
	Precipitate	31.3	31.0	Excess Ag
	Precipitate	33.2	31.7	Excess Ag
	Precipitate	38.6	34.1	Excess Ag
	Precipitate	40.6	33.7	Excess Ag
	Precipitate	48.6	33.4	Excess Ag
	Precipitate 5% of maximum	60.8	12.9	Excess Ag
Singer and Campbell (1955b)	Soluble complex	67.0	55.5	Excess Ag
	Soluble complex	70.6	56.5	Excess Ag
	Soluble complex	76.2	59.8	Excess Ag
	Soluble complex	80.8	61.5	Excess Ag
	Soluble complex	86.5	62.9	Excess Ag
	Soluble complex	91.0	64.5	Excess Ag

Goldberg (1952) to help check his equation (cf. Table 18). The same data were also used by Kabat (1961) to illustrate the precipitin reaction and appeared in his book as Table 1. They appear here in Table 19 as values recalculated in terms of mole fraction of antigen. The molecular weights of EA and anti-EA that were used in the recalculation of the Heidelberger-Kendall data were taken as 43,000 and 160,000, and the nitrogen contents of EA and anti-EA on a weight basis were assumed to be equal. The total moles of added antibody that, together with moles of added EA, were used to determine the total moles of added ingredients were calculated from the maximum precipitable antibody nitrogen as given in the paper.

The data of Singer and Campbell (1955b) for EA-anti-EA reactions in antigen excess were used to help establish the relationship of Figure 25 that has already been discussed. They also appear in Table 19 as the recalculated values in terms of mole fraction of antigen. The Singer-Campbell ratio r, the average ratio of bound antigen to bound antibody in a soluble complex formed in antigen excess, was already in molar form and was easily converted to mole fraction of EA. The mole fraction of antigen in the whole mixture (T) was obtained from the Singer-Campbell data by the formula

$$T = \frac{1}{1 + \frac{1}{r} - \frac{[Ag]}{r}}$$

where [Ag] equals the ratio of free antigen to total antigen as given by Singer and Campbell (1955b) and also by Singer (1957, 1965). The values for T and B are shown in the phase plot of Figure 27.

A number of interesting features appear in the graph. The first and most obvious are the extrapolated intercepts: 16.7 % at $T = 0$ and 66.7 % at $T = 100$ giving valences of 5 and 2 for EA and anti-EA. Goldberg's value for the valence of EA in his reworked data was also given as 5. The second feature is the sigmoid nature of the curve, indicating a change in phase. In antibody excess antigen precipitates antibody almost as if antibody were univalent. That the straight portion

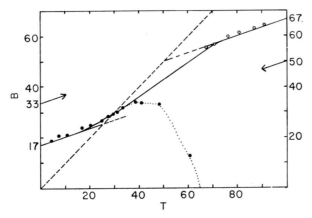

FIG. 27. Phase diagram of EA-anti-EA. *Closed circles* are calculated from data of Heidelberger and Kendall (1935d). *Open circles* are calculated from data of Singer and Campbell (1955b). The 45° *dashed line* is the line of equivalence. The *dotted line* connects precipitation data in antigen excess; not all bound antigen and antibody are represented by the *dotted line*, much of it, in fact, being in solution, and with a composition approaching the *open-circle* data of Singer and Campbell.

of the line (Fig. 27) in antibody excess is not identical to FS (Fig. 26) but slightly above it indicates some bivalent contribution but not nearly enough to approach the homogeneous line FD. As the line (Fig. 27) nears equivalence by approaching the line OP it changes slope upwards. This is correlated with a change in the nature of the precipitate from a flocculent to a much more stable form that is characteristic of precipitates formed with optimal proportions of antigen and antibody at equivalence. At equivalence there are between 2 and 3 antibody molecules per antigen molecule. Probably many of these form double antibody links between antigen molecules to create polymer units of

$$[Ag–(Ab)_2–Ag–(Ab)_2–Ag–(Ab)_2–]_n$$

Such formation would be consistent with the findings of Feinstein and Rowe (1965), whose electron microscope pictures of ferritin-anti-ferritin (Fig. 24) revealed double strands between many pairs of ferritin molecules. Each strand was interpreted as representing the backbone of the tertiary structure of an antibody molecule. *The strands were most prominent at equivalence.*

The precipitates formed in antigen excess start decreasing in size and strength as total antigen increases. Commensurate with this are a breakdown in precipitate composition and a solubilization of complexes. The antigen composition of the precipitates reaches a maximum soon after equivalence and then decreases sharply. At the point where the mole fraction of added antigen is about double that of equivalence ($T = 60$), a precipitate is obtained in which the effective antigen valence is 8! Such precipitates probably would be most resistant to breakdown in large antigen excess and would be the last to be seen. From this point on, called the region of inhibition, all complexes are in solution.

Starting at $T = 100$ and moving towards equivalence from the antigen excess side, the curve of combination (Fig. 27) moves away from the hapten-binding univalent line DGH (Singer's a complex) towards one linking antigen and antibody in aggregates such that at equivalence both antigen and antibody would be equimolar ($B = 33.3$ at $T = 0; B = 66.7$ at $T = 100$). This would be suggestive of units of

$$(–Ag–Ab–Ag–Ab–Ag–Ab–)_n$$

in which both components were bivalent.

One interpretation of the data as shown in Figure 27 would be that a change in phase occurs between equivalence and inhibition in Zone 1 of antigen excess. The change would be characterized by the weakening of a stable double-antibody linked chain and the creation of a single-

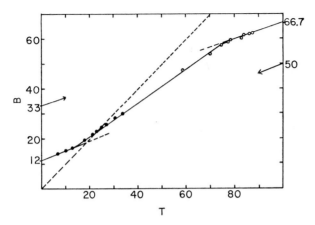

F<small>IG</small>. 28. Phase diagram of SA-anti-SA. *Closed circles* are calculated from data of Kabat and Heidelberger (1937) for HSA-anti-HSA. *Open circles* are calculated from data of Singer and Campbell (1955b) for BSA-anti-BSA. The 45° *dashed line* is the line of equivalence.

antibody linked chain as antigen excess increases. The former would be less soluble than the latter so that another feature or parameter of change in phase would be change in solubility.

Similar recalculations have been carried out for the HSA-rabbit anti-HSA precipitin system that was investigated by Kabat and Heidelberger (1937) and which was reproduced in Chapter 2 of Kabat's book (1961) as Table 5. Soluble complex data for HSA-anti-HSA were not available, but the Singer-Campbell data for bovine serum albumin were felt to be closely enough related to illustrate a point. These are shown in Figure 28. Once again antibody forms essentially univalent bonds with antigen in antibody excess. In this stage in the precipitate there would probably be found little interlinking of antigen molecules. The valence of HSA appears to be 7 in this system, as given by Goldberg (1952), rather than 6 as reported by Kabat (1961). As the equivalence point is neared an upswing in antibody binding is seen with stabilization of precipitates through interlinking of aggregates. At equivalence antibody to antigen ratios are between 3 and 4. Because of the higher valency of HSA over that of EA and a higher molecular weight, equivalency occurs at a lower mole fraction of added antigen.

The Singer-Campbell data again tend to follow a line between antibody and antigen bivalency, indicating chains of alternating single components; however, the complexes formed in lowest antigen excess show definite change in phase. It is interesting that they fall on the same line as the Kabat-Heidelberger data taken from equivalency through antigen excess.

The Heidelberger-Kabat data for EA-anti-EA that have already been discussed were obtained during a first course of injections of an individual rabbit, No. 3.87. Course I was followed by two more courses, designated II and III, with the last giving rise to an antiserum whose globulin was 40.7 % specifically precipitable with egg albumin. Phase diagrams were prepared from precipitation data for sera II and III as well as for I and appear together in Figure 29. The precipitation equations, similar to those of Table 16 for pneumococcal polysaccharide S-III, showed increasing values of R (ratio of antibody N to egg albumin N at the midpoint of equivalence).

$$\text{Serum 3.87 I: Ab N/EA N} = 15.8 - 83 \text{ EA N}$$

$$\text{II: Ab N/EA N} = 20.4 - 96 \text{ EA N}$$

$$\text{III: Ab N/EA N} = 24.8 - 111 \text{ EA N}$$

In the phase diagrams of Figure 29 it can be seen that as the immunizations continued an increase in effective valence of egg albumin was obtained, first from 5 to 6 and then to 7. *It is obvious that effective antigen*

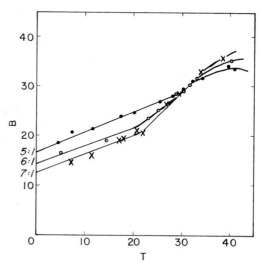

Fig. 29. Phase diagram of EA-anti-EA. All data are from Heidelberger and Kendall (1935d). *Closed circles*, Course I serum from rabbit 3.87; *open circles*, Course II serum from the same rabbit; *crosses*, Course III serum from the same rabbit. Effective antigen valence for Course I is 5; for Course II, 6; for Course III, 7.

valence is not a constant property of antigens, even for the same animal.
Increase in valence in this situation may have arisen from increased
avidity of antibody or from additional determinant groups in egg albumin that had become recognized by the rabbit. The Course III antibody
was shown not to have arisen from an anamnestic response but from a
gradual increase in precipitable antibody even though a month had
elapsed between Course II and Course III. The mole fractions of antigen
in the precipitates formed in antibody excess tended to fall on the *FRS*
lines, thus indicating absorption of antibody as a univalent molecule
to an *f*-valent antigen. At the line of equivalence all three preparations
followed the line to form equivalent zones, but the Course III antibody
reached equivalence at the lowest *T* value and left equivalence at the
highest *T* value. Course II antibody was intermediate and Course I
antibody had the narrowest zone. Course III precipitate in antigen
excess appeared most resistant to antigenic dissolution and had the
highest antigenic composition. Course II precipitate had intermediate
stability and Course I precipitate had the least.

*In spite of the variations in reactivity of the three antibody preparations
all three had one thing in common: a common mid-point of equivalence.*

This fact more than any other that is so readily revealed in the phase
diagrams forms the basis of quantitative immunochemistry. The mid-
point of the zone of equivalence is a most precise measure of antigen-
antibody interaction. At this point either component can be determined
by means of the other with as much accuracy as modern analytical
techniques will allow. *Because of this the Heidelberger-Kendall precipitin
technique remains one of the most reliable methods of titration in biochemistry.*

One may have wondered how immunochemistry had been so analyti-
cally successful in the face of heterogeneity at every turn. The reason
is self-evident: heterogeneity which is so prominent in regions of antigen
and antibody excess becomes minimal at equivalence. This is the law
of equivalence. By the same token, investigations of the nature of antibody and antigen combining sites are least rewarding at equivalence.
For this reason, more than any other, quantitative immunochemistry
with its dependence on precipitation analysis was developed to a high
degree long before modern instrumentation established the structural
nature of its principal reagent—the bivalent rabbit antibody.

To demonstrate by example how application of the law of equivalence
can help in analyzing results, the very excellent and precise work of
Ishizaka, Ishizaka, and Sugahara (1961) on the nature of co-precipitating
antibody is re-evaluated. Rabbit antibody against egg albumin was

prepared and quantitative precipitin analyses performed. The results of the titration are shown as *filled circles* in Figure 30. Co-precipitating antibody is defined as that which will bind antigen but will not, in itself form precipitates with antigen. It will, however, co-precipitate with ordinary antibody. It was prepared in the experiments described here by 13 successive precipitations in antibody excess with egg albumin until no visible precipitate would form when the supernatant fluid was titrated with antigen. Calculation reveals the actual process as shown in Table 20. Actual analysis gave 11.2 moles of antibody per ml remaining in the supernatant fluid; the calculation as shown in the table gives 11.5 moles/ml. (The Danysz phenomenon is amply demonstrated here since, by 14 successive absorptions where T varied from 2 to 4%, 3,040 moles of antigen removed 15,580 moles of antibody out of a total of 17,420 whereas at optimal proportions with reactants added all at once 4,880 moles of antigen would have been required to do the same job.)

When co-precipitating antibody plus precipitating antibody were mixed and titrated, the results shown by the *open circles* in Figure 30 were obtained. (See also Table 21.) It can be seen that the mixture of antibodies produced the same effect as the precipitating antibody alone and that therefore the co-precipitating antibody was acting no differently. The effective antigen valence can be seen to be 5 and the mid-point of equivalence to be 30 as in the Heidelberger-Kendall experiments with their Course I anti-EA antibody.

As shown by electrophoresis, co-antibody gave a single peak; when mixed with antigen it gave three peaks, indicating that it would complex with antigen. Furthermore, when it was precipitated from antigen excess with half-saturated ammonium sulfate, antigen came down with it as a

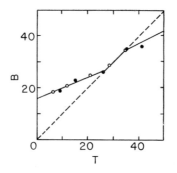

Fig. 30. Phase diagram of EA-anti-EA. All data are calculated from Ishizaka, Ishizaka, and Sugahara (1961). *Closed circles* are for precipitating antibody; *open circles* are for co-precipitating plus precipitating antibody.

TABLE 20

Successive Precipitations of Anti-EA from 160 ml by Small Amounts of Added EA*

EA Added	Anti-EA Remaining	EA in Mixture	EA in Precipitate	Anti-EA Removed
moles		*mole %*		*moles*
392	21,400	1.8	17.0	4,000
349	17,400	2.0	17.0	3,000
326	14,400	2.2	17.5	2,500
302	11,900	2.5	17.5	2,100
279	9,800	2.8	17.5	1,700
256	8,100	3.1	17.8	1,230
233	6,870	3.3	17.8	1,030
209	5,840	3.5	17.9	1,040
186	4,800	3.7	17.9	860
163	3,940	4.0	18.0	580
139	3,360	4.0	18.0	610
116	2,750	4.0	18.0	500
93	2,250	4.0	18.0	410
	1,840			

(Constructed from data of Ishizaka, Ishizaka, and Sugahara, 1961.)

* Total moles of EA added = 3,043; total moles of anti-EA added = 21,400; total moles of EA removed = 3,043; total moles of anti-EA removed = 19,560; 1,840 moles of anti-EA/160 ml = 11.5 moles/ml remaining. Actual analysis showed that 11.2 moles/ml remained.

TABLE 21

Precipitation Characteristics of Precipitating and Co-precipitating Anti-EA Antibodies with EA

Precipitating Antibody			75% Precipitating Antibody + 25% Co-precipitating Antibody		
T	*B*	Investigators' comments	*T*	*B*	Investigators' comments
8.9	18.6	Excess Ab	6.2	18.3	Excess Ab
15.0	23.0	Excess Ab	11.6	20.8	Excess Ab
26.1	26.5	Trace Ab	20.8	24.5	Trace Ab
34.6	34.4	Neither	28.3	28.6	Neither
41.4	35.6	Excess Ag	34.5	34.5	Trace Ag
58.7	43.0	Excess Ag	51.4	31.4	Excess Ag

(Constructed from data of Ishizaka, Ishizaka, and Sugahara, 1961.)

complex. With this evidence Ishizaka *et al.* (1961) concluded that co-precipitating antibody was unbound and free after the exhaustive precipitations with antigen to remove precipitating antibody, but that it would bind with antigen added to it to form complexes in antigen excess. To this author it did not seem logical that an antibody should display binding properties on one side of the equivalence zone but not on the other. Calculations were therefore made of the T values at which co-precipitating antibody was prepared and at which, in antigen excess, it was subjected to electrophoretic analysis. The first value was $T = 4$; the second, $T = 79$. In the first case antigen would be coated with antibody but antibody would be effectively univalent and antigen particles would not be linked. This is shown in the phase diagram by the fact that the data in antibody excess coincide with the FRS line from an antigen valence of 5 at $T = 0$ to an antibody valence of 1 at $T = 100$. Such aggregates at $T = 4$ would be expected to precipitate partially but not wholly. It is much more likely, therefore, that this particular co-precipitating antibody is the soluble portion of normal antigen-antibody complexes formed at $T = 4$. When mixed with regular antibody it "co-precipitates" not only at equivalence but at $T = 6.2$. That it should co-precipitate at this point but not at $T = 4$ during its initial preparation is unlikely. Electrophoretic homogeneity would be expected at this point since aggregation of particles would not yet be expected. The charge would be due mainly to exposed IgG molecules. At $T = 79$ the variety of complexes observed by Singer and Campbell would be expected with $Ab(Ag)_2$ and $(Ab)_2(Ag)_3$ predominating.

One of the main points that Ishizaka et al. wished to make in their paper—that the peak skin-sensitizing activity of complexes occurs in those formed in moderate antigen excess—becomes strengthened and most reasonable as a result of application of the law of equivalence. On the antibody-excess edge of equivalence haptenic groups are less exposed in the Phase I type of precipitate with its higher antibody coverage, probable double-antibody links, and tight structure. On the antigen-excess edge of equivalence and on into moderate antigen excess the Phase II type of complexes would be more open, probably linked through single antibody molecules, covered with less antibody, and loosened structurally. As such the Phase II type would offer the maximum exposure of antigen-antibody surface and of the linkages themselves, both of which would be expected to increase the biological effects of skin sensitization. In large antigen excess the loose structure would be broken down, small aggregates would be formed, and the biological effects would be decreased. The other major point that Ishizaka et al. wished to make—that co-precipitating as well as precipitating antibodies can form skin-sensitizing complexes with antigen—is also strengthened and made clear. Since co-precipitating and precipitating antibody (in this instance) are probably one and the same antibody, no difference could be expected.

That soluble complexes of EA-anti-EA can and do exist in regions of high antibody excess is demonstrated unequivocally by Forster and Weigle (1963). Thus, it would seem that the present analysis of the data given by Ishizaka *et al.* (1961) may have some merit.

REFERENCES

Arrhenius, S. (1907). The precipitins and their antibodies. In *Immunochemistry*, Macmillan (New York, 309 pp.), pp. 263–299.

Burnet, F. M. (1931). The interactions of staphylococcus toxin anatoxin and antitoxin. J. Pathol. Bacteriol. *34:* 471–492.

Cooper, G., Edwards, M., and Rosenstein, C. (1929). The separation of types among the pneumococci hitherto called group therapeutic antiserums for those types. J. Exptl. Med. *49:* 461–474.

Danysz, J. (1902). Contribution a l'étude des propriétés et de la nature des mélanges. Des toxines avec leurs antitoxines. Ann. Inst. Pasteur *16:* 331–345.

Farr, R. S. (1958). A quantitative immunochemical measure of the primary interaction between I*BSA and antibody. J. Infect. Diseases *103:* 239–262.

Feinstein, A., and Rowe, A. J. (1965). Molecular mechanism of formation of an antigen-antibody complex. Nature *205:* 147–149.

Forster, O., and Weigle, W. O. (1963). The formation of soluble complexes in the region of antibody excess with protein antigens and their rabbit antibodies. J. Immunol. *90:* 935–941.

Goebel, W. F. (1935). Chemo-immunological studies on the soluble specific substance of pneumococcus. II. The chemical basis for the immunological relationship between the capsular polysaccharides of types III and VIII pneumococcus. J. Biol. Chem. *110:* 391–398.

Goldberg, R. J. (1952). A theory of antibody-antigen reactions. I. Theory for reactions of multivalent antigen with bivalent and univalent antibody. J. Am. Chem. Soc. *74:* 5715–5725.

Heidelberger, M. (1939). Quantitative absolute methods in the study of antigen-antibody reactions. Bacteriol. Rev. *3:* 49–95.

Heidelberger, M. (1956). Chemical constitution and immunological specificity. Ann. Rev. Biochem. *25:* 641–658.

Heidelberger, M., and Avery, O. T. (1923). The soluble specific substance of pneumococcus. I. J. Exptl. Med. *38:* 73–79.

Heidelberger, M., and Avery, O. T. (1924). The soluble specific substance of pneumococcus. II. J. Exptl. Med. *40:* 301–316.

Heidelberger, M., Gaudy, E., and Wolfe, R. S. (1964). Immunochemical identification of the aldobiuronic acid of the slime of *Sphaerotilus natans*. Proc. Natl. Acad. Sci. U. S. *51:* 568–569.

Heidelberger, M., and Goebel, W. F. (1927). The soluble specific substance of pneumococcus. V. On the chemical nature of the aldobiuronic acid from the specific polysaccharide of Type III pneumococcus. J. Biol. Chem. *74:* 613–618.

Heidelberger, M., and Hobby, G. L. (1942). Oxidized cotton, immunologically specific polysaccharide. Proc. Natl. Acad. Sci. U. S. *28:* 516–518.

Heidelberger, M., and Kabat, E. A. (1937). Chemical studies on bacterial agglutination. III. A reaction mechanism and a quantitative theory. J. Exptl. Med. *65:* 885–902.

Heidelberger, M., and Kabat, E. A. (1938). Studies on antibody purification. II.

The dissociation of antibody from pneumococcus specific precipitates and specifically agglutinated pneumococci. J. Exptl. Med. *67:* 181–199.

Heidelberger, M., Kabat, E. A., and Shrivastava, D. L. (1937). A quantitative study of the cross reaction of Types III and VIII pneumococci in horse and rabbit antisera. J. Exptl. Med. *65:* 487–496.

Heidelberger, M., and Kendall, F. E. (1929). A quantitative study of the precipitin reaction between Type III pneumococcus polysaccharide and purified homologous antibody. J. Exptl. Med. *50:* 809–823.

Heidelberger, M., and Kendall, F. E. (1935a). The precipitin reaction between Type III pneumococcus polysaccharide and homologous antibody. II. Conditions for quantitative precipitation of antibody in horse sera. J. Exptl. Med. *61:* 559–562.

Heidelberger, M., and Kendall, F. E. (1935b). The precipitin reaction between Type III pneumococcus polysaccharide and homologous antibody. III. A quantitative study and a theory of the reaction mechanism. J. Exptl. Med. *61:* 563–591.

Heidelberger, M., and Kendall, F. E. (1935c). A quantitative theory of the precipitin reaction. II. A study of an azoprotein-antibody system. J. Exptl. Med. *62:* 467–483.

Heidelberger, M., and Kendall, F. E. (1935d). A quantitative theory of the precipitin reaction. III. The reaction between crystalline egg albumin and its homologous antibody. J. Exptl. Med. *62:* 697–720.

Heidelberger, M., and Kendall, F. E. (1936). Quantitative studies on antibody purification. I. The dissociation of precipitates formed by pneumococcus specific polysaccharides and homologous antibodies. J. Exptl. Med. *64:* 161–172.

Heidelberger, M., and Kendall, F. E. (1937). A quantitative theory of the precipitin reaction. IV. The reaction of pneumococcus specific polysaccharides with homologous rabbit antisera. J. Exptl. Med. *65:* 647–660.

Heidelberger, M., Kendall, F. E., and Scherp, H. W. (1936). The specific polysaccharides of types I, II, and III pneumococcus. A revision of methods and data. J. Exptl. Med. *64:* 559–572.

Heidelberger, M., Kendall, F. E., and Teorell, T. (1936). Quantitative studies on the precipitin reaction. Effect of salts on the reaction. J. Exptl. Med. *63:* 819–826.

Heidelberger, M., and Pedersen, K. O. (1937). The molecular weight of antibodies. J. Exptl. Med. *65:* 393–414.

Heidelberger, M., and Rebers, P. A. (1960). Immunochemistry of the pneumococcal types II, V, and VI. I. The relation of type VI to type II and other correlations between chemical constitution and precipitation in antisera to type VI. J. Bacteriol. *80:* 145–153.

Heidelberger, M., Treffers, H. P., and Mayer, M. (1940). A quantitative theory of the precipitin reaction. VII. The egg albumin-antibody reaction in antisera from the rabbit and horse. J. Exptl. Med. *71:* 271–282.

Heymann, H., Manniello, J. M., and Barkulis, S. S. (1963). Structure of streptococcal cell walls. I. Methylation study of C-polysaccharide. J. Biol. Chem. *238:* 502–509.

Ishizaka, K., Ishizaka, T., and Sugahara, T. (1961). Biologic activity of soluble antigen-antibody complexes. VI. Complexes in equivalence and in excess antibody. J. Immunol. *86:* 590–598.

Jones, J. K. N., and Perry, M. B. (1957). The structure of the type VIII pneumococcus specific polysaccharide. J. Am. Chem. Soc. *79:* 2787–2793.

Kabat, E. A. (1939). The molecular weight of antibodies. J. Exptl. Med. *69:* 103–118.

Kabat, E. A. (1961). *Kabat and Mayer's Experimental Immunochemistry*, 2nd Ed., Charles C Thomas (Springfield, Ill., 905 pp.).

Kabat, E. A., and Berg, D. (1953). Dextran—an antigen in man. J. Immunol. *70:* 514–532.

Kabat, E. A., and Heidelberger, M. (1937). A quantitative theory of the precipitin reaction. V. The reaction between crystalline horse serum albumin and antibody formed in the rabbit. J. Exptl. Med. *66:* 229–250.

Kabat, E. A., and Pedersen, K. O. (1938). The molecular weights of antibodies, anti-Types I and III. Science *87:* 372–373.

Klinman, N. R., Rockey, J. H., Frauenberger, G., and Karush, F. (1966). Equine anti-hapten antibody. III. The comparative properties of γG- and γA-antibodies. J. Immunol. *96:* 587–595.

Markowitz, H., and Heidelberger, M. (1954). Chemical modifications of the specific polysaccharide of Type III pneumococcus and their immunologic effects. J. Am. Chem. Soc. *76:* 1313–1316.

Marrack, J. R. (1938). *The Chemistry of Antigens and Antibodies*, Her Majesty's Stationery Office (London, 194 pp.), pp. 169–175.

Pappenheimer, A. M. (1940). Anti-egg albumin antibody in the horse. J. Exptl. Med. *71:* 263–269.

Rebers, P. A., and Heidelberger, M. (1961). The specific polysaccharide of type VI pneumococcus. II. The repeating unit. J. Am. Chem. Soc. *83:* 3056–3059.

Reeves, R. A., and Goebel, W. F. (1941). Chemoimmunological studies on the soluble specific substance of pneumococcus. V. The structure of the type III polysaccharide. J. Biol. Chem. *139:* 511–519.

Singer, S. J. (1957). Physical-chemical studies on the nature of antigen-antibody reactions. J. Cellular Comp. Physiol. *50:* Suppl. 1, 51–78.

Singer, S. J. (1965). Structures and function of antigen and antibody proteins. In *The Proteins*, 2nd Ed., Vol. III, Neurath, H., ed., Academic Press (New York, pp. 269–357), p. 291.

Singer, S. J., and Campbell, D. H. (1951). The valence of precipitating rabbit antibody. J. Am. Chem. Soc. *73:* 3543–3544.

Singer, S. J., and Campbell, D. H. (1952). Physical chemical studies of soluble antigen-antibody complexes. I. The valence of precipitating rabbit antibody. J. Am. Chem. Soc. *74:* 1794–1802.

Singer, S. J., and Campbell, D. H. (1953). Physical chemical studies of soluble antigen-antibody complexes. II. Equilibrium properties. J. Am. Chem. Soc. *75:* 5577–5578.

Singer, S. J., and Campbell, D. H. (1955a). Physical chemical studies of soluble antigen-antibody complexes. III. Thermodynamics of the reaction between bovine serum albumin and its rabbit antibodies. J. Am. Chem. Soc. *77:* 3499–3504.

Singer, S. J., and Campbell, D. H. (1955b). Physical chemical studies of soluble antigen-antibody complexes. V. Thermodynamics of the reaction between ovalbumin and its rabbit antibodies. J. Am. Chem. Soc. *77:* 4851–4855.

Sugg, J. Y., Gaspari, E. L., Fleming, W. L., and Neill, J. M. (1928). Studies on immunological relationships among the pneumococci. I. A virulent strain of pneumococcus which is immunologically related to, but not identical with typical strains of type III pneumococci. J. Exptl. Med. *47:* 917–931.

Taylor, G. L. (1931). The results of some quantitative experiments on the serum precipitation reaction. J. Hyg. *31:* 56–83.

Tiselius, A., and Kabat, E. A. (1938). Electrophoresis of immune serum. Science *87:* 416–417.

Tiselius, A., and Kabat, E. A. (1939). An electrophoretic study of immune sera and purified antibody preparations. J. Exptl. Med. *69:* 119–131.

von Dungern, E. (1903). Bindungsverhältnisse bei der Präzipitinreaktion. Zentr. Bakteriol. Parasitenk. Abt. I Orig. *34:* 355–380.

9

Inhibition of Precipitation

The principle of hapten inhibition as developed by Landsteiner in his serological searches for specificity involved the qualitative method of reacting an antibody with free hapten and of observing the drop in precipitability of the antibody with hapten-bound precipitating protein. The immunization would be made with hapten coupled to one protein such as horse or chicken serum protein; the precipitin test would be made with hapten coupled to another such as egg albumin. By this method he was able to obtain information concerning cross-reactivity of closely related haptens with antibody and to draw qualitative conclusions concerning the nature and extent of specificity (cf. Chapter 5.3).

Attempts have been made to establish the method of hapten inhibition of precipitation reactions upon a more quantitative footing, but considerations of the law of equivalence show how difficult this would be. For example, Pauling, Pressman, and Grossberg (1944) in the development of their quantitative theory built their concepts around a bivalent antibody reacting with a bivalent antigen and found that the theory agreed well with their evidence. The problem was that their experimental evidence was unusual in terms of the law of equivalence.

They chose a polyhaptenic substance, antigen **XXX**, as test antigen to precipitate with their anti-R or anti-R' sera:

Antigen XXX

R = diazotized *p*-arsanilic acid
R' = diazotized *p*-(*p*-aminophenylazo)phenylarsonic acid

It can be seen that antigen **XXX** was bivalent with respect to the arsanilic acid groups and the *p*-(*p*-aminophenylazo)phenylarsonic acid groups.

When anti-R antibody was reacted with antigen **XXX** an equivalence zone was obtained in which 769 μg of antibody protein (i.e., 4.8×10^{-9} mole) precipitated with 32×10^{-9} mole of antigen. In terms of the mole fraction of antigen in the precipitate, expressed as percent, this would be 87 %! Whereas in the usual equivalence zone there might be found 2, 3, or 4 *antibody* molecules per antigen (giving 33, 25, or 20 mole fraction %), here are reported data that calculate to 6 or 7 *antigen* molecules per antibody (0.17 or 0.14 antibody molecule per antigen). With antibody assumed to be bivalent in the Pauling theory, the heavy precipitation of antigen would have to be attributed either to non-specific antigen absorption, to polymeric formation in antigen XXX, or to some spontaneous antigen precipitation. In any of these cases, the hapten inhibition data that were obtained through use of this system would have little meaning in terms of inhibition of antibody binding. Even in the case of the R'-azo-ovalbumin, which contained 2 % arsenic and therefore contained 6 R' groups per molecule of egg albumin, 377 μg of antibody protein precipitated 185 μg of the R'-protein to form 562 μg of precipitate at equivalence. In molar quantities this would be 2.36×10^{-9} mole of antibody and 4.12×10^{-9} mole of R'-ovalbumin (molecular weight taken as $42,000 + 2,900 = 44,900$). In mole percent antigen the value would be 63.6 %. According to the law of equivalence such a composition would be very close to the univalent antigen line in its reaction with bivalent antibody. Precipitation would not be expected in such cases except for antigen molecules that were already close to insolubility and needed only one or two antibody molecules to bring them down. Whatever the reason, the hapten inhibition data obtained through the use of R'-ovalbumin would also appear to lack validity. Indeed, Epstein, Doty, and Boyd (1956) showed that antibody precipitation of a number of other bivalent haptens was rare and that aggregates containing more than 2 antibody molecules were difficult to achieve. They wondered if perhaps precipitation, when it did occur, might be due merely to hapten association.

That precipitation of antihapten antibody with hapten coupled to protein *can* follow a normal pattern is revealed in the more precise data of Nisonoff, Winkler, and Pressman (1959). Antibody was prepared in rabbits against bovine IgG (BGG) coupled with *p*-azobenzoate, the antiserum globulin fraction was prepared, anti-BGG was absorbed out by a BGG-anti-BGG-specific absorbent, and the remaining antibody, non-reactive for the most part with BGG, was tested in a precipitation titration with BGG-*p*-azobenzoate. From data converted to mole fraction of antigen bound and mole fraction of total antigen, an equivalence point of 30.3 % was obtained as compared with an equivalence point of 29.5 % before absorption. An antigen valence of 4 was obtained, points in antibody excess fell on the line towards univalent antibody ($B = 50$

when $T = 100$, $B = 20$ when $T = 0$), a change in precipitation phase was noted at equivalence, and points in antigen excess fell on the line towards bivalent antibody. Ordinary BGG, in its reaction with the un-absorbed anti-BGG-p-azobenzoate antibody, had a valence of 3 and an equivalence point of 40 %. Analysis by the equilibrium dialysis technique showed that the interaction of the antihapten antibody with hapten was unaffected by pre-absorption of the antibody with BGG absorbent since binding of hapten remained constant whether or not absorption took place.

Hapten inhibition of precipitation was not attempted with this system since there were other techniques such as equilibrium dialysis that would provide better information. But one can see that even with such a workable precipitating system as obtained by Nisonoff *et al.* (1959) there would be problems in interpretation of quantitative inhibition data. Consider antibody and antigen at an equivalence point of 33 mole % antigen. If hapten is added before antigen to neutralize 50 % of the binding sites, the effective number of antibody molecules is reduced 50 %, the mole percent of antigen with respect to effective antibody is increased to 50 %, and the ordinary zone of precipitation inhibition is near at hand. Reduction in the amount of precipitate formed (the usual measure of hapten inhibition) when hapten is present would therefore be caused not only by reducing the effective number of binding sites but also by moving the system away from equivalence far into the zone of antigen excess. In this region antigen may be still combined with anti-body but rendered soluble. Therefore, not all precipitation inhibition would be due to hapten but partly to a shift in composition of the re-actants.

Even if the soluble antigen-antibody complexes as well as the pre-cipitates in antigen excess were analyzed and somehow differentiated from soluble hapten-antibody complexes, there would be the additional problem of change in precipitate phase that would interfere in quanti-tation. Some of the hapten added at equivalence would contribute to opening up the tight multi-antibody linked structure (or preventing its formation) to form the loose single-antibody linked structure without changing the amount of antigen-antibody complex that would precip-itate. Composition of the complex would move along the line of equiva-lence. Hence, precipitation itself would not be inhibited, and, in fact, should show an increase as a result of the amount of absorbed hapten during the very early phases of hapten inhibition titration.

For the reasons given here the enormous amount of quantitative equi-librium, thermodynamic, and heterogeneity data that have been obtained through the method of hapten inhibition of precipitation must be held suspect and only qualitative conclusions concerning specificity and cross-reactivity should be drawn in the original manner of Landsteiner.

REFERENCES

Epstein, S. I., Doty, P., and Boyd, W. (1956). A thermodynamic study of hapten-antibody association. J. Am. Chem. Soc. *78:* 3306–3315.

Nisonoff, A., Winkler, M. H., and Pressman, D. (1959). The similar specificity of the combining sites of an individual antibody molecule. J. Immunol. *82:* 201–208.

Pauling, L., Pressman, D., and Grossberg, A. L. (1944). The serological properties of simple substances. VII. A quantitative theory of the inhibition by haptens of the precipitation of heterogeneous antisera with antigens, and comparison with experimental results for polyhaptenic simple substances and for azo-proteins. J. Am. Chem. Soc. *66:* 784–792.

10

Chemical Modification and Labeling of Antibodies

1. Introduction

Affinity labeling is the method of choice, whenever possible, to investigate the nature of the combining site. Although, as discussed in Chapter 5, the method is still in its infancy, it has already provided valuable information about chemical groupings associated with the active antibody sites that conform to certain haptenic structures. Many methods of modifying and/or labeling antibody molecules exist, however, that do not specifically involve site chemistry: esterification of carboxyl groups; acetylation, guanidation, succinylation, carbobenzoxylation, p-iodobenzoylation, dinitrophenylation, etc., of amino groups; iodination and diazotization of tyrosinyl and histidyl groups; reduction of disulfide bonds; unstable iodination and general oxidation of sulfhydryl groups; introduction of additional sulfhydryl groups with N-acetylhomocysteine thiolactone; and several other similar organic and inorganic processes.

There is generally one of two main concerns in the use of such processes: (1) the hope that antibody activity can in some way be progressively reduced by the introduction of specific chemical groups, or (2) the hope that antibody activity can be preserved in spite of the chemical reactions. Investigations of the first type are mainly concerned with the chemical nature of the active site; in the other, with incorporation of radioactive, fluorescent, and electron- and neutron dense labels, with attachments to insoluble adsorbents, and with interlinkages with a variety of substances through bridging compounds. In either case one has to know something of the nature of the particular antibody activity that is being measured before drawing conclusions as to the effect of the groupings that have been introduced. If the method involves precipitation at equivalence and the modification of antibody results in a decrease in precipitability, there are a number of possible explanations for the inactivation:

1. The active site may have been attacked directly.

2. The tertiary structure supporting the antibody site may have been affected, preventing access to the site.

3. The antibody may have been rendered univalent, thus preventing complex formation.

4. Soluble complex formation may have taken place, but subsequent precipitation prevented by factors such as increased charge that would prevent aggregation into precipitable form.

5. Precipitation may not have been ultimately prevented, but merely slowed down to a considerable degree.

In all of these situations one assumes that a precipitation titration has been carried out and that an equivalence point for each modified antibody preparation has been obtained with each antigen under study. If equivalence has not been established, there would also be an additional possible explanation for inactivation:

6. The precipitating system may have been shifted away from the optimal proportions necessary for equivalence precipitation.

The first three explanations would be possible whether the method of measurement involved complex precipitation, soluble complex formation, or simple univalent hapten-antibody interaction. The fourth, fifth, and sixth explanations would be possible only in the case of precipitation. Affinity labeling alone among the known procedures would determine actual site involvement. Protection experiments (chemical modifications while sites were protected by haptenic groups) would limit the explanations to the first two. Titrations in far antigen excess would determine whether the third was involved. If the last three were involved but not the first three, the chemical modifications should result in no loss of haptenic binding activity, only loss in precipitability.

The manner in which precipitation (but not binding) might be affected by chemical modification would require careful analyses in all regions of the precipitation titration. The exquisite experiments of Schlamowitz (1958), in fact, demonstrate how carefully precise one must and can be in establishing the nature of the precipitation reaction before attempting chemical modification studies. The antigen in this case was the enzyme, dog intestinal alkaline phosphatase. The antibody was prepared in rabbits. Enzyme activity happened to be unaffected by the antibody so that it could be measured whether precipitated with antibody, complexed with antibody but still soluble, or free from antibody. Soluble complexes could be isolated by precipitation with horse anti-rabbit IgG; phosphatase activity in them would indicate the extent of complex formation. Thus, all forms of antigen could be accounted for, the advantage over ordinary nitrogen determinations of antigen being the sensitivity of antigen detection through its functional enzyme activity. A soluble prozone of complexed antigen in antibody excess was revealed (ordinarily difficult to establish), variable precipitation times were obtained depending on the proportion of added constituents (over 4 days in the regions of excess antigen or antibody), and maximum precipitation times for minute amounts of components (sometimes over 2 weeks in the cold) were measured under carefully controlled conditions. Kabat (1961), who was obviously as impressed with this work as the author, concluded his discussion of it with the statement that "it is advisable to establish proper conditions for maximum precipitation in studying new antigen-antibody systems." The author, in endorsing this statement, should like to point out that a chemically modified antibody should be treated as if it were a new antibody; and its combination with antigen, as a new system requiring more than cursory attention. If such care had always been exerted, we might have been spared the many incorrect conclusions that have been drawn from chemical modification studies on precipitating systems.

2. Iodination

The popularity of iodination of antibody results from its chemical simplicity of reaction, the ease of incorporation of radioactivity into the antibody molecule through the use of radioiodine, and the selectivity of tyrosine as its main (though by no means sole) target of attack. The difficulty of ascribing loss of antibody activity to iodination of a tyrosine within the active site can be readily understood when it is remembered that rabbit IgG contains 56 tyrosine residues per molecule (molecular weight of 160,000), and that, therefore, a total of 112 atoms of iodine could be incorporated before exhaustion of all tyrosine residues. It is true that surface tyrosines would be most amenable to attack and with them those that are near active-site centers, but, as was described earlier, the heavy-chain tyrosines that are most closely associated with combining-site activity may escape iodination that heavily attacks light-chain tyrosines.

In addition to the 56 tyrosines there are also 16 histidines, 14 methionines, and 20 tryptophans that can react with iodine, and long before all tyrosines become exhausted many of these other residues will become involved.

The data of M. E. Koshland, Englberger, and Gaddone (1965) answer one question negatively once and for all: Is tyrosine a universally essential amino acid for site activity? They prepared two different antihapten antibodies, one against p-azophenyltrimethylammonium ion (Apz) and the other against *p*-azophenylarsonate (Rpz). Anti-Apz antibody with an average of *140 iodine atoms* per molecule still retained 15 % of its binding sites and 30 % of its binding affinity even after treatment with 10 M urea for 3 hours to expose all available tyrosine groups. In contrast to this, anti-Rpz had lost all its activity by the time *60 iodine atoms* had been added (Fig. 31). Equilibrium dialysis measurements were made of the binding capacity of anti-Apz, and the familiar Scatchard plots of binding capacity against hapten concentration gave the typical Karush-type curves (Fig. 32).

The data of Johnson, Day, and Pressman (1960) on the effect of iodination on antibody activity are not so simply interpretable, the reason being that precipitation and other complicated systems were used as the basis of measurement: precipitation of egg albumin and BSA, hemolysis of red cells, *in vitro* binding of radioiodinated antibody to red cells, and *in vivo* binding of radioiodinated antibody to rat kidney and liver were used. Only one thing was clear: that levels of iodination over an average of *two* iodine atoms per molecule resulted in progressive loss of precipitating activity with 50 % loss occurring in most instances if only an average of eight were introduced and essentially 100 % loss at a level of 30 atoms per molecule (Fig. 33). The application of the results to trace labeling with radioactive iodine was apparent, indicating that certain precipitating and absorption systems could be followed equally well with classical or radioactive methods of measurement as long as no more than two atoms of iodine were introduced per antibody molecule.

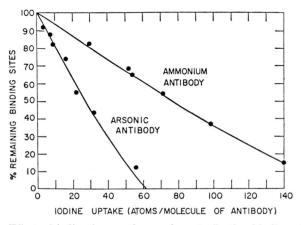

FIG. 31. Effect of iodination on the number of effective binding sites in ammonium and arsonic antibodies. (M. E. Koshland, Englberger, and Gaddone, 1965.)

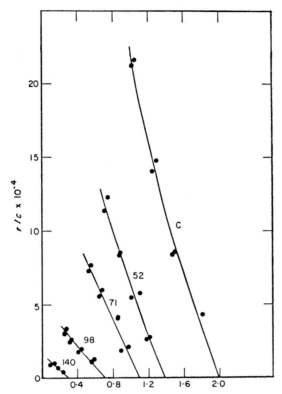

FIG. 32. Scatchard plot, r/c vs. r, showing the effect of iodination on the binding activity of ammonium antibody. The parameter r is the number of hapten molecules bound per molecule of antibody. The parameter c is the concentration of free hapten at equilibrium. Curve C represents untreated antibody. The *numbers* beside the remaining curves represent the atoms of iodine substituted per molecule of antibody. (Koshland, Englberger, and Gaddone, 1965.)

Aside from contributing to the practical matters of effective trace labeling, and confirming the results of Powell (1958) on *in vivo* binding of radioantibody in tissues, which was its main object, the paper contributed only confusion to theory. For example, the statement was made that only one antibody combining site was required for *in vivo* and *in vitro* binding to cells and tissues and for hemolysis. Then it was noted that an initial plateau of 100% activity occurred until two atoms of iodine per molecule were reached and that therefore the first atom of iodine inactivated site 1, the second attacked the same tyrosine in site 1 to form the diiodo derivative, and that not until the third iodine atom did site 2 become involved.

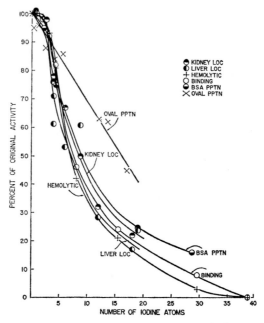

Fig. 33. Effect of iodination on antibody activity. Ordinate is percentage of original activity which remains after iodination. Abscissa is the average number of iodine atoms per 160,000 molecular-weight unit of rabbit IgG. (Johnson, Day, and Pressman, 1960.)

It is now quite apparent that few of the iodine atoms were essentially involved in site inactivation in the Johnson-Day-Pressman (1960) experiments and that even tertiary structures were probably not invoked at low levels. In the precipitating systems some factor critically connected with precipitation *per se*, not preliminary binding and soluble complex formation, must have been the target. In the *in vivo* and *in vitro* absorption experiments similar factors may very well have been operative since the same supersensitivity to iodination was observed. It was only assumed but never put to test that *in vivo* tissue binding, *in vitro* red cell binding, and *in vitro* red cell hemolysis required only univalent antibody, but even if found to be true (also open to question) this assumption may prove to be a mere non sequitur in the interesting observable decrease in antibody activity resulting from so few atoms of iodine. From the plot in Figure 31 one can see that even in the case of an antibody (anti-Rpz) whose hapten-binding activity could be seriously hampered by iodination, a level of 5–10 atoms per molecule resulted in only a 10–20% decrease in activity and a level of 30 atoms in only 50% reduction.

There is no doubt that the nature of the effects of iodination upon precipitins, agglutinins, hemolysins, etc., are by no means known, and that the reasons for the relative sensitivity of such types of antibody activity to iodination will not be simply found in active-site chemistry. Much more investigation will be required.

A hint that iodination of active sites was not particularly or even critically responsible for the loss in precipitating activity was contained in the egg-albumin system that was studied in depth by Johnson et al. (1960). Precipitin titrations were carried out at all levels of iodination using both nitrogen and radioactive iodine as measures of antibody present. Antibody precipitated at high levels of iodination had a ratio of nitrogen to iodine much the same as the non-precipitated antibody at those same levels. If iodination of sites alone were responsible for over-all decreases in activity, those antibodies that were active should have shown higher $N:I$ ratios. Moreover, construction of phase diagrams from data given in the paper showed that the zone of equivalence (beginning at 31 mole % antigen) and the effective egg albumin valence (3) were unaffected by iodination. The titration lines at all levels of iodination were superimpossible.

3. Acetylation

Marrack and Orlans (1954) subjected precipitins to acetylation and found that although power to precipitate was destroyed, power to co-precipitate was retained. Similarly, Nisonoff and Pressman (1958) found that antibody that failed to precipitate hapten-azoprotein after acetylation still retained full hapten-binding capacity when tested by equilibrium dialysis. Thus, the earlier experiments of Chow and Goebel (1935) on loss of precipitating power of anti-S-I pneumococcal antibody by acetylation could be explained by precipitation interference phenomena rather than active-site sensitivity, and the experiments of Singer (1955) on lack of effect of acetylation upon soluble complex formation in the BSA-anti-BSA system could be brought into harmony with general immunological experience rather than kept apart from it.

4. Labeling of antibodies

Recipes for labeling antibodies are extensive and varied, and oftentimes neglectful of basic principles inherent in all antibody labeling processes. The first principle is perhaps the one most flagrantly abused, the principle that *a labeled antibody is a chemically modified one.* To delineate the many processes of chemical modification behind labeling processes would require many hundreds of pages, and the effort would be less than comprehensive at best because of the rapid expansion in modification studies that would outpace the compilation. The examples of iodination and acetylation hopefully will serve to point up the essential problems.

The second principle can be stated as a question. *What is the effect of the particular chemical modification upon the particular antibody activity?* The principle can work both ways. Some investigators will waste time, effort, and energy in being too cautious while others will be wasteful because they are not cautious enough. A few atoms of iodine difference per antibody molecule would have little over-all effect on reproducibility of hapten-binding experiments with radioiodinated antihapten antibody; it would make all the difference in the world on reproducibility of precipitation experiments. This is all too obvious, one would say; yet how many experiments of this type have really been satisfactorily conducted with those other two popular antibody labels, fluorescein and ferritin? Fluorescein with its fluorescent properties in ultraviolet light is a powerful tool for cytological and histochemical investigations of antibody localization in cells and tissues. Likewise, ferritin with its electron-dense properties is a comparable tool in electron microscopy. Yet their use by the average tissue investigator appears to be based more on blind faith in some magic recipe than on rational confidence in a scientific formula and realization of its limitations. The effects of chemical modification may be expected to vary from one system to the next, and labeling processes likewise.

A seemingly elementary principle in labeling that is frequently overlooked, particularly as one moves away from the more classical methods of antibody measurement to those novel ones where labeled antibodies find their greatest use, is the fact that *non-specific as well as antibody protein becomes labeled*. Modern immunochemistry tends to exploit the purified and concentrated antibody and leave the non-specific behind in its investigations of antibody reactions with known antigens. The analyst working with unknown antigen systems, against which he has developed antibody, cannot always use purified antibody, for his purification process would depend on some knowledge of the antigens and their behavior under various conditions. How, then, can he tell the difference between labeled non-specific protein and labeled antibody, or, stated in a different way, how does he know when labeled antibody is present because of its specific binding to some unknown antigen and when it is present because of non-specific binding? The plain truth is that he may not know. It is not always possible to control for non-specific effects. The analytical usefulness of antigen-antibody reactions that depend on equivalence for optimum observable activity stems from the fact that such reactions are peculiar to specific antigen-antibody combinations. It would be very unusual indeed to observe such behavior from non-specific globulin. As one moves away from equivalence-dependent reactions, however, one also moves away from immunological uniqueness. Binding *per se* is not a peculiar property of antigens and antibodies, but a much more general one.

To detect differences between labeled non-specific globulin and labeled specific antibody one needs to be able to recover and concentrate the labeled material and to demonstrate an increase in percentage binding when it is reapplied to antigen. The problem here is that so-called non-specific globulins may also show an increase. Much more antibody may be recovered and a higher percentage of the recovered material may then react with antigen, but the difference between it and non-specific globulin will still remain a quantitative rather than a qualitative one.

REFERENCES

Chow, B. F., and Goebel, W. F. (1935). The purification of the antibodies in type I antipneumococcus serum, and the chemical nature of the type-specific precipitin reaction. J. Exptl. Med. *62:* 179–202.

Johnson, A., Day, E. D., and Pressman, D. (1960). The effect of iodination on antibody activity. J. Immunol. *84:* 213–220.

Kabat, E. A. (1961). *Kabat and Mayer's Experimental Immunochemistry*, 2nd Ed. Charles C Thomas (Springfield, Ill., 905 pp.), pp. 40, 41.

Koshland, M. E., Englberger, F. M., and Gaddone, S. M. (1965). Evidence against the universality of a tyrosyl residue at antibody combining sites. Immunochemistry *2:* 155–125.

Marrack, J. R., and Orlans, E. S. (1954). The effects of acetylation of amino groups on the reactions of antigens and antibodies. Brit. J. Exptl. Pathol. *35:* 389–401.

Nisonoff, A., and Pressman, D. (1958). Loss of precipitating activity of antibody without destruction of binding sites. Science *128:* 659–660.

Powell, A. E. (1958). Degree of iodination and localizing activity of rabbit anti-kidney γ-globulin. J. Am. Chem. Soc. *79:* 4246.

Schlamowitz, M. (1958). The reaction of dog intestinal phosphatase with its antibodies in the region of excess antibody. J. Immunol. *80:* 176–181.

Singer, S. J. (1955). On the chemical structure of the reactive sites of antibody molecules. Proc. Natl. Acad. Sci. U. S. *41:* 1041–1045.

11

Antibody Purification by Absorption and Elution Processes

1. Specificity and cross-reactivity

Antiserum globulins are generally mixtures of antibodies against a multitude of determinant groups admixed with non-specific or normal globulin. Antibody reagents are most useful if they can be rendered monospecific for the particular antigen or determinant group in question. Two different approaches can be made to the problem of monospecificity: (1) neutralizing and removing all antibodies except the desired ones, an indirect approach, or (2) removing the desired antibodies through inter-action with purified antigen and subsequently recovering them. In the first approach antigen against the undesirable antibodies is generally available and can be used to "absorb out" all but the desired antibodies. In the second, antigen against the desired antibodies is available and can be used to "absorb out" the specific entities. Elution processes then must be used to liberate the antibodies for further analytical use.

The Landsteiner-van der Scheer experiments with GIL (cf. Chapter 5) are an example of the indirect method in which the specific antibody used for testing was that which was left over after absorption with cross-reacting antigen. The Kreiter-Pressman experiment with GIL (cf. Chapter 5) is an example of the direct method in which the test antibody is actively separated from specific antigen before it is used. The two experiments were not as complementary to each other, however, as they would appear to be upon first glance (and herein lies one of the greatest pitfalls in working with purified antibody). By exhaustive absorption of anti-GIL antisera with one or the other of the two haptens G and L, Landsteiner and van der Scheer eliminated cross-reactive antibodies that would react with either hapten. If such antibodies were present they could not be discovered by this method.[1] On the other hand, by absorp-

---

[1] The quantitative precipitin test could measure the amount of cross-reactivity. If the sum of separate precipitins brought down in one tube by G and in another

tion of anti-GIL antibodies to a column of an immunoadsorbent containing GIL and eluting separately with individual haptens, Kreiter and Pressman obtained preparations that were certain to contain cross-reactive antibodies. Thus, if specific antibodies were present they could not be discovered by this method.

If the elimination of cross-reacting antibodies is crucial and mono-specificity highly desired, there is no way to avoid the use of cross-reacting antigen to absorb out the unwanted antibodies. This is true not only for antisera and whole antiserum globulins but also for highly concentrated and purportedly purified antibody. If a profile of cross-reactivity and specificity is desired, there is also no way to avoid use of cross-reacting antigens. Only through their use can specificity be de-lineated. It is not surprising, therefore, that a knowledge of the extent and nature of cross-reactivity may be most crucial as well as most difficult.

Although the term "purified antibody" will be used in the ensuing discussion, it must be understood that in most instances the term "concentrated antibody" would have been better. What is usually meant by purification is the elimination of most non-specific protein and retention of most antibody protein that will react with a particular antigen. Elimination of cross-reactive antibody requires additional absorption procedures.

2. Elution from specific precipitates

The process that might be expected to provide the purest antibody would be one involving precipitation of antigen and antibody at equivalence. Thus, the Heidelberger-Kendall procedure of precipitating in dilute salt and eluting in strong salt (cf. Chapter 8) gave rise to a horse anti-S-III antibody that was 90–98 % precipitable. Yield of antibody depended upon the difference in quantitative precipitation in the two salt solutions and the reversibility attained in bringing the precipitin medium from a dilute to a strong salt concentration. Generally speaking the Heidelberger-Kendall method was less successful when rabbit antisera, for example, were used. Yields were far lower and specific precipitability was not always so high. For elutions of antipolysaccharide antibodies, however, salt dissociation techniques would be the first method of choice.

Other conditions must be changed to separate antiprotein antibodies

by L were equal to the amount brought down in a third tube by GIL, there would be little indication of cross-reaction; if the sum were much greater, the presence of cross-reacting antibody would be dominant; if the sum were much smaller, the presence of antibody specific for intact GIL would be indicated.

from their specific precipitates, but there is frequently less rationale for the particular method finally chosen than in the antipolysaccharide system. (Heidelberger and Kendall, it will be remembered, predicted the conditions and the yield for eluted S-III from quantitative precipitation data.) General methods include application of heat, changes in pH, shifts in ionic strength, enzymatic digestion, and addition of large quantities of free hapten. What one frequently does not know is whether a particular method, arbitrarily chosen and relatively satisfactory, is successful because of some reversal in antigen-antibody combination or because of denaturation and destruction of antigenic determinants.

One of the problems, in those cases where dissociation takes place without antigenic destruction, is the separation of free antibody from free antigen since both may tend to solubilize after dissociation. Chromatographic, electrophoretic, ultracentrifugal, and molecular-sieve techniques can be used in many cases, but, particularly with dissociations at pH 2.5–3.5, physical separations often present manipulative problems. Singer, Fothergill, and Shainoff (1959) worked out a general procedure to circumvent this problem. The protein antigen, e.g., egg albumin, was treated with N-acetylhomocysteine thiolactone to increase its sulfhydryl content several-fold without affecting its precipitability with antibody. After specific precipitates had been prepared and washed, they were dissociated at pH 2.5, at which time 3,6-bis(acetoxymercurimethyldioxane) was added. The organic mercurial compound, by virtue of its dimeric form, would react with and cross-link the antigenic sulfhydryl groups and cause the antigen to precipitate. The supernatant fluid was then brought back to neutrality and isotonicity and found to be as much as 90 % precipitable (in terms of nitrogen content).

Dissociation of antibody from specific precipitates formed with unknown antigens poses a somewhat more difficult problem. The method of Smith, Tozer, Gallop, and Scanes (1962) for separating antigen-antibody complexes in agar gel and the method of Tozer, Cammack, and Smith (1962) for dissociating the formed precipitates in salt-free media with aqueous carbon dioxide would appear to be as generally applicable as any method yet available under such circumstances.

3. Absorption and elution processes involving insoluble antigen

One of the reasons why the Singer-Fothergill-Shainoff technique has not been given widespread use may be due to the recent flood of insolubilized antigens. Absorption of antibody by an insoluble antigen and elution from it solves the problem of antigen solubility following dissociation of specific precipitates.

Some of the earliest artificially created insoluble immunoadsorbents were Landsteiner's hapten azostromata, such as the GIL-azostromata referred to in Chapter 5, which utilized the diazotization process to link a soluble hapten with insoluble red cell stroma. Various natural insoluble antigens that were used as immunoadsorbents included fibrin, collagen, casein, cell wall materials, and vascular tissues. Rendering such proteins as ovalbumin and BSA insoluble without destroying their antigenicity, however, posed a problem. Confronted with this problem, Campbell, Luescher, and Lerman (1951) turned their attention to the possibility of coupling antigens to diazotized p-aminobenzylcellulose and were encouraged by the results. Although many better immunoadsorbents have since been prepared both in Campbell's laboratory and elsewhere (Weliky and Weetall, 1965), these initial experiences proved to be a turning point in antibody purification techniques. Gurvich, Kuzovleva, and Tumanova (1962) and Moudgal and Porter (1963) in particular improved the methods for preparation of cellulose-antigen complexes to the point where absorption of antibody was considerably higher than non-specific globulin. Absorbent capacity was also increased.

An even more attractive method for antibody recovery through absorption on and elution from immunoadsorbents was worked out by Weliky, Weetall, Gilden, and Campbell (1964). Avoiding the process of diazotization, carboxymethyl-cellulose and the amino groups of antigens were joined as amides in the presence of N,N'-dicyclohexylcarbodiimide (DCC) under extremely mild conditions.

$$\begin{array}{ccc} \text{Cellulose} & & \text{Cellulose} \\ | & & | \\ \text{O} & & \text{O} \\ | & & | \\ \text{CH}_2 \; + \; \text{RNH}_2 \; \xrightarrow{\;\text{DCC}\;} & \text{CH}_2 \; + \; \text{H}_2\text{O} \\ | & & | \\ \text{C=O} & & \text{C=O} \\ | & & | \\ \text{OH} & & \text{HN—R} \end{array}$$

Non-specific uptake of protein from normal serum was considerably less with the CM-cellulose-antigen columns than with the former p-aminobenzyl-cellulose-antigen (PAB-cellulose-antigen) columns (Table 22); purity of antibody isolated from the columns was good (Table 23), and recoveries from the columns were much better (Table 24). Interestingly enough, *no success was obtained in recovering anti-DNP antibodies from CM-cellulose-lysine-DNP by elution at pH 2.3*, and when specific precipitates prepared from BSA-DNP and anti-DNP antibodies were likewise treated at pH 2.3, *no dissociation was observed*. Thus, not even acid elution can be considered as a universal method of dissociating antibodies.

TABLE 22

Nonspecific Protein Recovery from Columns

Column	Serum Added	Protein Eluted at pH 2.3
CM-cellulose-BSA	3 ml, normal rabbit	0.010 mg/ml serum
PAB-cellulose-BSA	2 ml, normal rabbit	0.117 mg/ml serum

(From Weliky, Weetall, Gilden, and Campbell, 1964.)

TABLE 23

Purity of Isolated Antibody from CM-Cellulose Columns

Column	Serum Added	Serum Ab	Total Ab	Ab in Effluent	Protein Eluted	Ab Precipitable in Eluate
	ml	*mg/ml*	*mg*	*mg*	*mg*	*%*
CM-cellulose-BSA	5.0	3.52	17.60	12.00	3.65	90.2
CM-cellulose-HGG	5.0	2.25	11.25	7.42	3.52	97.4

(From Weliky, Weetall, Gilden, and Campbell, 1964.)

TABLE 24

Recovery of Antibody from CM-Cellulose Columns

Column	Ab Retained by Column	Ab Recovered from Column	Over-all Yield	Total Ab Accounted for
	mg	*%*	*%*	*%*
CM-cellulose-BSA	5.60*	59	19	87
CM-cellulose-HGG	3.83	89	30	97

(From Weliky, Weetall, Gilden, and Campbell, 1964.)

* Some minor miscalculations appeared in the original article which have been corrected here.

A variant of the carboxymethyl-cellulose column has now been prepared which provides a benzidine bridge for azo coupling (Weetall and Weliky, 1964). Several other types of insoluble carriers besides cellulose have been used as the backbones for haptens and antigen, and many more will undoubtedly be developed. Prominent among these are antigenic attachments to ion-exchange resins of the sulfonic and carboxylic types (Isliker, 1953) and to polyaminopolystyrene (Manecke and Gilbert, 1955; Gyenes, Rose, and Sehon, 1958), and to physical entrapment in highly cross-linked synthetic polymers such as those from acrylamide (Bernfeld and Wan, 1963). Attachment to insoluble proteins themselves is now relatively common; and, through controlled denaturation processes of soluble proteins that preserve determinant groups, insoluble natural vehicles are sometimes possible (Hirata and Campbell, 1965).

While emphasis in the literature has been upon efficiency in describing the virtues of any particular immunoabsorbent—its capacity for absorbing antibody, its non-specific level of absorption, and its release of antibody during elution—, there has been little correlation of absorption and elution processes with antigen-antibody reaction kinetics. Can one, for example, tacitly assume that antibody absorption to insoluble antigens, whether on columns or in batch processes, involves only one antibody site? In an excess antigen environment antibody would certainly be expected to have a tendency to be absorbed bivalently as long as antigenic density was high. For subsequent elution of antibody one might expect that monovalently bound antibody would be easier to elute and less likely to be damaged. Perhaps less efficient absorption of antibody by low antigen-density absorbent might provide conditions for more efficient elution. In an excess-antibody environment, antibody would be expected to be absorbed monovalently even on high-density absorbents, and non-specific globulin would be expected to be absorbed only minimally. Efficiency again would be low in terms of the initial starting material since in antibody excess not all antibody would be absorbed, but the quality of the eluted product might be considerably improved.

Ideal absorption should follow the same pattern as the Danysz phenomenon (Chapter 8.5). By adding very small amounts of absorbent to an antibody preparation at intervals of every few minutes, and continuing the process until exhaustion of antibody activity in the soluble phase, one would have utilized the antigenic capacity of an absorbent to the maximum, absorbed antibody monovalently, minimized non-specific absorption of other proteins, and recovered purified antibody through elution in maximum yield. Column separations are obviously less applicable here than batch separations by centrifugation. Fractionation for various cross-reacting antibodies would ideally follow the same pattern with absorption by the most distantly related antigens occurring first. There are very few examples provided in the literature of such processes, but one is mentioned which St. Groth (1963) calls *sequential fractionation:*

> Probably all of us who tried dissociating antigen-antibody complexes had the same experience . . . yields of 30–40 per cent. What is particularly worrying here is that this fraction of antibody is, almost by definition, the least complementary and therefore the least interesting fraction of the population. We have found a way round this by what we call *sequential fractionation* of sera. The method was worked out on influenza viruses where, by special

providence, a new antigenic mutant is given unto us, practically each year. We pick out half-a-dozen of these, order them according to their serological crossing with the immunizing antigen, and absorb the serum first with the most distant relation. The mixture is passed through an ultrafilter which retains virus but not antibody; the filtrate absorbed with the next virus in the queue and the residue dissociated at pH 3.5 in a glycine buffer. This procedure is carried through until we reach the homologous antigen, and we find that by pooling the dissociated fractions, we recover 100 per cent activity and have achieved an over thousandfold purification in terms of antibody/non-antibody nitrogen.

If the purification process involving absorption and elution is not preceded by isolation of a particular class of immunoglobulin, the purified product may be expected to contain more than one type of "carrier" of antibody activity. For example, an individual horse serum that Klinman, Rockey, and Karush (1965) prepared against p-azophenyl-β-lactoside (anti-Lac) was found to contain at least six distinct immunoglobulins, each one of which carried anti-Lac activity: IgM, Ig-10S, IgA, IgG-a, IgG-b, and IgG-c. Through application of hapten-binding curves it was found that the association constant for the IgG components in this serum was 4.24×10^5 M^{-1} at 25°C whereas the association constant for IgA in the same serum was two orders higher, 10^7 M^{-1} (Rockey, Klinman, and Karush, 1964). The Ig-10S components had an association constant of 10^5 M^{-1} also, thus leaving IgA with the strongest average binding characteristics. One could well imagine that if these various antibodies were absorbed by an insoluble absorbent and then dissociated by some elution process (that did not destroy the hapten), absorption of the IgA component would be most complete but elution of it would be most difficult to achieve. After 6 months, when the serum in the horse gave rise to both IgG and IgA with association constants greater than 10^7 M^{-1} (Klinman, Rockey, Frauenberger, and Karush, 1966), the absorption-elution pattern would be yet a different one.

One is reminded of the work of Porter and Pappenheimer (1939; cf. Chapter 5) in which horse IgA (antitoxin against diphtheria) was adsorbed bivalently on a monomolecular surface of antigen (toxin). An additional layer of antigen could therefore not be adsorbed. On the other hand, horse IgM (anti-S-III) was adsorbed monovalently on an undersurface of polysaccharide and therefore could and did adsorb another layer above itself to form, in effect, a sandwich between two layers of polysaccharide. Asymmetry of binding-site placement on the IgA molecule was postulated by Porter and Pappenheimer to explain this phenomenon. Now, of course, we regard other immunoglobulins as asymmetrical with respect to binding-site placement. Why do these not also show a tendency to adsorb bivalently on a film or on a given antigen? The answer is that perhaps they do on occasion. Whether they do or do not may depend upon binding strength and the association constant. A clue to such a possibility is the contrast between ease of dissociation of S-III-anti-S-III, achieved by mere increase in ionic strength, and the complete lack of dissociation of toxin-antitoxin, even when the pH of the medium is brought to 3.6 (Pappenheimer, Lundgren, and Williams, 1940).

One will remember that Weliky et al. (1964) were unable to dissociate rabbit anti-DNP at pH 2.3 from CM-cellulose columns containing that hapten attached through lysine bridges. Contrast this with the ease of dissociation of rabbit anti-BSA and rabbit anti-HGG antibodies from similar columns. When one recalls that anti-DNP antibodies have a tendency to display extremely high association constants there is every likelihood that the two phenomena are related. One would, in fact, predict that rabbit IgG with a high association constant for DNP would also show bivalent and asymmetrical absorption on a monomolecular film of DNP.

There is certainly no assurance that antibody absorption would involve only one of its sites, an assumption that was made, for example, by Johnson, Day, and Pressman (1960) (cf. Chapter 10.2). If the association constant were high enough and the antigenic density adequate, both sites of an antibody could conceivably be bound to adjacent determinants in a single strand of absorbing material. Elution of such antibodies would be rather ineffective and the yields would be low. The same assumption—that antibody is effectively univalent in absorption studies— was made by Hughes-Jones, Gardner, and Telford (1962, 1963) in their work on the kinetics of anti-c and anti-D isoantibodies by red cells. By studying rates of absorption and elution of ^{131}I antibody by red cells, estimates could be made of association constants at equilibrium for anti-c (from 1.9×10^7 to 1.8×10^8 M^{-1}) and for anti-D (from 1.4×10^8 to 7.2×10^{10} M^{-1}). The rate reaction constants for the forward and the reverse reactions were generally of the order of 10^4 M^{-1} sec^{-1} and 10^{-4} sec^{-1}, respectively, in the case of anti-c; and were 10^5 M^{-1} sec^{-1} and 10^{-5} sec^{-1}, respectively, in the case of anti-D. Thus, the effective equilibrium constant $K_a = k_f/k_r$, although of the same order as anti-DNP with DNP hapten (cf. Chapter 7), reflected an extremely slow rate of dissociation. The rate of association would unquestionably have been faster in homogeneous solution, so that the published values might be expected to be minimal. They do reflect an association that could very well involve at least occasional binding of the two sites of an antibody molecule to a single cell. *If the tendency in a red cell-anti-red cell system were for a given antibody to bind bivalently to single cells, agglutination would not occur and the antibody would be described as incomplete.* Factors that would tend to decrease binding somewhat and/or increase dissociation would be expected to favor univalent antibody absorption and to result in agglutination. The author is not suggesting that all incomplete antibodies be regarded in this way, but only that such possibilities not be discounted.

Absorption-elution processes that result in purification of antibody may abound, but the underlying mechanisms to explain such processes remain for the most part obscure. The speculative account given here hopefully will help to renew interest in finding out what these mechanisms are even if it turns out that the speculation itself finds little additional support. One thing is true and not speculative: the better comprehension one has of the foundations of immunochemistry the better prepared one is to devise new methods of purification, to improve old ones, and to exploit the increased potential of the antibody reagent brought about by purification.

REFERENCES

Bernfeld, P., and Wan, J. (1963). Antigens and enzymes made insoluble by entrapping them into lattices of synthetic polymers. Nature *142:* 678–679.

Campbell, D. H., Luescher, E., and Lerman, L. S. (1951). Immunologic adsorbents. I. Isolation of antibody by means of a cellulose-protein antigen. Proc. Natl. Acad. Sci. U. S. *37:* 575–578.

de St. Groth, S. F. (1963). Discussion on sequential fractionation. Ann. N. Y. Acad. Sci. *103:* 609–610.

Gurvich, A. E., Kuzovleva, O. B., and Tumanova, A. E. (1962). The use of immunosorbents in the form of suspensions for the determination of the absolute antibody content. Biokhimiya *27:* 246–251.

Gyenes, L., Rose, E., and Sehon, A. H. (1958). Isolation of antibodies on antigen-polystyrene conjugates. Nature *181:* 1465–1466.

Hirata, A. A., and Campbell, D. H. (1965). The use of a specific antibody adsorbent for estimation of total antibody against bovine serum albumin. Immunochemistry *2:* 195–205.

Hughes-Jones, N. C., Gardner, B., and Telford, R. (1962). The kinetics of the reaction between the blood-group antibody anti-c and erythrocytes. Biochem. J. *85:* 466–474.

Hughes-Jones, N. C., Gardner, B., and Telford, R. (1963). Studies on the reaction between the blood-group antibody anti-D and erythrocytes. Biochem. J. *88:* 435–440.

Isliker, H. C. (1953). Purification of antibodies by means of antigens linked to ion exchange resins. Ann. N. Y. Acad. Sci. *57:* 225–238.

Klinman, N. R., Rockey, J. H., and Karush, F. (1965). Equine antihapten antibody. II. The γ-G (7Sγ) components and their specific interaction. Immunochemistry *2:* 51–60.

Klinman, N. R., Rockey, J. H., Frauenberger, G., and Karush, F. (1966). Equine anti-hapten antibody. III. The comparative properties of γG- and γA-antibodies. J. Immunol. *96:* 587–595.

Manecke, G., and Gilbert, K. E. (1955). Serologische spezifische Adsorbentien. Naturwissenschaften *42:* 212–213.

Moudgal, N. R., and Porter, R. R. (1963). The use of antigen-cellulose suspensions for the isolation of specific antibodies. Biochim. Biophys. Acta *71:* 185–187.

Pappenheimer, A. M., Jr., Lundgren, H. P., and Williams, J. W. (1940). Studies on the molecular weight of diphtheria toxin, antitoxin, and their reaction products. J. Exptl. Med. *71:* 247–262.

Porter, E. F., and Pappenheimer, A. M., Jr. (1939). Antigen-antibody reactions between layers adsorbed on built-up stearate films. J. Exptl. Med. *69:* 755–765.

Rockey, J. H., Klinman, N. R., and Karush, F. (1964). Equine antihapten antibody. I. $7S\beta_{2A}$- and $10S$ γ_1-globulin components of purified anti-β-lactoside antibody. J. Exptl. Med. *120:* 589–609.

Singer, S. J., Fothergill, J. E., and Shainoff, J. R. (1959). A new and general method for the isolation of anti-protein antibodies. A. Am. Chem. Soc. *81:* 2277–2278.

Singer, S. J., Fothergill, J. E., and Shainoff, J. R. (1959). A general method for the isolation of antibodies. J. Am. Chem. Soc. *82:* 565–570.

Smith, H., Tozer, B. T., Gallop, R. C., and Scanes, F. S. (1962). Separation of antigens by immunological specificity. 1. Method for separating individual antigen-antibody complexes from mixed antigens and antibodies. Biochem. J. *84:* 74–80.

Tozer, B. T., Cammack, K. A., and Smith, H. (1962). Separation of antigens by immunological specificity. 2. Release of antigen and antibody from their complexes by aqueous carbon dioxide. Biochem. J. *84:* 80–92.

Weetall, H. H., and Weliky, N. (1964). New cellulose derivatives for the isolation of biologically active molecules. Nature *204:* 896–897.

Weliky, N., and Weetall, H. H. (1965). The chemistry and use of cellulose derivatives for the study of biological systems. Immunochemistry *2:* 293–322.

Weliky, N., Weetall, H. H., Gilden, R. V., and Campbell, D. H. (1964). The synthesis and use of some insoluble immunologically specific adsorbents. Immunochemistry *1:* 219–229.

12
Antigenicity

1. Introduction

The ever-widening circle of substances that can be investigated by immunochemical techniques presents new challenges and demands new approaches at every turn; however, as long as an antibody reagent can be prepared against a determinant of a particular unknown there is every good chance that a technique can be worked out for that unknown's detection and measurement. Production of the antibody reagent in the first place is the most critical phase, and antibody production depends on antigenicity. The limitations of analytical immunochemistry are therefore the limitations of antigenicity. The present chapter, rather than cataloguing the expansive realm of antigens, shows by example some of the interesting problems that have been encountered by investigators and that have not already been touched upon in earlier chapters.

2. Antigenicity of synthetic polypeptides and protein determinants

In Chapter 7 it was shown that immunogenicity to polypeptides depended in part upon the species selected for antibody production and, within a given species, upon the presence of certain amino acids in at least small amounts. The lack of immunogenicity in rabbits or guinea pigs to copolymers of D-amino acids was attributed by Maurer (1963) to the inability of these animals to degrade the unnatural synthetic polymers enzymatically. The degree of antigenicity of copolymers of L-amino acids in these animals was attributable to the degree of rigidity within the macromolecules (Maurer, 1962). The introduction of an amino acid such as tyrosine which enhanced antigenicity did not wholly direct specificity to the newly introduced amino acid but sometimes shifted the effective determinant groups to one or another already present (Maurer, Gerulat, and Pinchuck, 1964). For example, the glutamic acid residues became most expressive in $Glu_{58}Lys_{38}Tyr_4$ whereas all moieties became expressive in $Glu_{42}Lys_{28}Ala_{30}$.

The precipitin test is not the most sensitive method of detection of antigenicity; thus, passive cutaneous anaphylaxis (PCA) is frequently used. The problem with the latter method is that is frequently involves a different immunoglobulin from the one involved in precipitin reactions. For biological tests the PCA globulin is probably more significant than the precipitin; for immunochemical purposes, the precipitin is more important. The work of Buchanan-Davidson, Stahmann, and Dellert (1959) suggests that the apparent weak antigenicity of synthetic polypeptides, as measured by precipitin reactions, may be partly a property of the polymers themselves. Antibodies would form precipitates with BSA and fibrinogen even when not precipitable with the homologous synthetic polypeptides against which they were made. Decreasing ionic strength to 0.05 from physiological conditions would frequently result in specific precipitates of polyglutamic acids with its antibody. The problem was therefore not in production of antibody, i.e., in antigenicity, but in production of an antibody that would form as strong a bond with its homologous antigen as with natural cross-reacting substances. *Thus, a substance may be better at eliciting an antibody than reacting with it later on.*

On the other hand, a substance may sometimes be poor at eliciting an antibody but quite cross-reactive with other antibodies formed against some of its determinant groups. Fuchs and Sela (1963) noted, for example, that antigenic sites that were buried within the matrix of synthetic polymers and inaccessible as biosynthetic sites would nevertheless cross-react with antibodies formed against substances closely related chemically.

Antigenicity of polypeptides is therefore an involved concept not readily measured by a simple or single reaction of homologous antigen with homologous antibody. Recognizing this, Gill and Doty (1960) began a systematic study of synthetic peptide-anti-peptide interactions that has led them into exploring the nature of precipitation reactions with the synthetic compounds. A sweeping study was that of Gould, Gill, and Kunz (1964), in which the electrostatic properties contributing to binding were most prominent. Glutamic acid in antibody and lysine in the synthetic antigen were apparently involved, and the binding between them was completely stable at 55°C for 1 hour and at 45°C for 5 days. However, the precipitation of antibody by the synthetic antigen would not take place above 25°C! One would rather imagine that a phase study at equivalence would reveal differences in the molar composition of complexes formed above 25°C and those formed below.

Antigenicity of naturally occurring proteins can be even more difficult to assess than to synthetic ones. Landsteiner and van der Scheer (1940) recognized two possible explanations to fit their observations on the antigenicity of egg albumin and on the mixed cross-reactions of various antisera against it which gave rise to multiple, qualitatively distinct antibodies:

> For this, two not mutually exclusive explanations come into consideration: the presence in proteins of a number of different, perhaps similar, complex determinants, and the fact, established by previous results, that an antigenic grouping can call forth the formation of diverse antibodies.

The second part of the statement invoked the frequently mentioned phenomenon of heterogeneity. The first part anticipated what is only now becoming disclosed as two distinct and separable states: *microheterogeneity* and *multiple determinancy*. Microheterogeneity is actually heterogeneity among antigen molecules (as among immunoglobulin molecules) such as found by Korngold (1963) in human haptoglobins and by Rejnek, Bednarik, and Koci (1963) in human serum albumins. Multiple determinancy relates most often to specific chain or fragment antigens (such as in the light and heavy chains of immunoglobulins) that are found in many proteins. Ovary (1964) ascribed the immunogenicity of guinea pigs to human hemoglobin A to separated α- and β-chains, and to globin. Four types of determinants were disclosed—two reactive in β-chains, one in α-chains, and one in the intact molecule. The last-mentioned, interestingly enough, was more antigenic than the determinants shared with isolated chains. Lapresle and Webb (1965) found a human serum albumin fragment, resulting from trypsin degradation, that contained only one of the antigenic determinants of HSA. With a molecular weight of 6600 and tyrosine and tryptophan free (!), the fragment could still be coupled to p-aminobenzyl-cellulose to form an insoluble absorbent. Anti-HSA was absorbed by the material, eluted in acid, and shown to contain both IgG and IgM. The IgG antibodies, at least, were bivalent. Antibodies left behind could not be inhibited in their reaction with intact HSA.

These are proofs of what Hooker and Boyd strongly suspected in 1934 as a result of their studies with crystalline duck and hen egg albumins: "that in one molecule of a pure substance there may exist several antigenic determinants of diverse specificity." What is possible now and hopefully intended in immunochemical circles is to determine those areas of communal reactivity in a given type of substance derived from several species as opposed to the areas of specificity. The experiments of Weigle (1961) on the cross-reaction between anti-BSA and 11 heterologous mammalian serum albumins are exemplary. They included precipitation studies, determinations of antigen-antibody ratios of equivalence and in excess zones of antibody and antigen, interactions of albumin fragments, absorptions, double diffusion tests, and inhibitions. Radio-iodinated albumins were used in conjunction with the precipitations to determine completeness of antigen removal by antibody. Each albumin, it was concluded, shared certain related or identical determinant groups —a portion of the total number of types. To separate, identify, and structurally define the communal determinants is a goal that is well within the grasp of present immunochemical technology. The work of Metzger, Sharp, and Edelhoch (1962) on thyroglobulin fragments; Kaminski (1962) on fragmented human siderophilin; Miller and Feeney (1964) on a variety of intact avian egg white proteins; and Rangel (1965) on complexes and conjugates of bovine and equine serum albumins need only be extended in the way Weigle conducted his study to bring the questions of cross-reaction and specificity, of shared and unshared determinants, well into focus. Can these multiple determinants be separated into communal and specific parts? Progress toward routine preparation of monospecific antibodies might well be speeded if this question could be affirmatively answered.

Another way to investigate antigenicity is through chemical modification of antigens, either those used for immunization or those used for testing. The existence of multiple determinancy makes such studies difficult to interpret, however, unless antibodies against the separate determinants are also available. After Maurer and his colleagues had established the probable unimportance of $R-NH_3^+$ groups (through N-acetylated, guanidated, and deaminated derivatives of BSA) upon BSA-anti-BSA interaction, Ram and Maurer (1958) extended the study to O-acetylated derivatives, and found that the phenolic groups of BSA were also not particularly necessary for BSA-anti-BSA interaction. Moreover, antibodies cross-reactive with native BSA could be induced against the esterified form of BSA, indicating that the phenolic groups were not required for antigenicity. An updated version of these experiments would ask several questions: Would some types of determinants differ chemically from others such that chemical modification would inactivate some but not others? What would be the mode of reaction of monospecific antibodies (specific for each determinant) with chemically modified determinants? Could communal determinants be selectively attacked, leaving specific ones intact, and *vice versa?* What would be the effect of chemical modification upon the formation of hybrid antigens, such as visualized by Singer (cf. Chapter 7), and upon structural heterogeneity? Is the distribution of determinants relatively uniform with repeating units built into the polymeric structure, or is the distribution asymmetrical with certain chains and fragments thereof containing all of some determinants and none of others? Does the broadening of specificity through prolonged immunization [as noted by Ram and Maurer (1958) for their O-acetyl-BSA] stem from the increase in number of types of determinants that give rise to antibodies or to increased cross-reactivity of antibodies against the original number of determinants? During antigen-antibody reactions in antibody excess zones does the chemically modified antigen show an increase, a decrease, or no change in its effective antigenic valence when tested with a particular antiserum? Morton and Deutsch (1961) obtained an ovomucoid fragment (molecular weight 6500) from a papain digest of the native protein which completely inhibited specific precipitation of the intact protein with *its* antibody. Did this fragment contain a representative portion of all determinants in the intact molecule or could a different antiserum have revealed specific precipitability involving determinants not present in the fragment? What would be the effect of limiting the determinants of a native protein to one type (through inactivation of the others) upon the molar composition of complexes in the different zones of antigen-antibody titration? What alterations in phase diagrams would be found?

3. Phosphatidylglycerols

Lipid immunochemistry began in 1906, when Detre isolated Wasserman substance from normal organs with alcohol. The extract reacted as well in a complement-fixation reaction as did the spirochete *Treponema pallidum*. Michaelis (1907) confirmed Detre's findings, and Landsteiner, Müller, and Pötzl (1907) extracted a substance similar to Detre's from the spirochete itself. Although the substance was so widespread in nature as to be commonly referred to as "that ubiquitous antigen," it was found in particularly rich supply in beef heart and was named *cardiolipin* by Pangborn (1942). Paradoxically, cardiolipin was not only the first and the most ubiquitous lipid to be extracted, but it was also the most unique in structure and the most peculiar in antigenicity. There are some even today who will argue that cardiolipin least of all should be regarded as an antigen—and they would be essentially correct, for it is really a hapten. Unlike *p*-aminobenzoic acid, however, which needs to be firmly coupled to a protein to behave as a determinant in immunogenic processes, cardiolipin need only be mixed with other compounds to express itself strongly as a hapten. In its reaction with antibody *in vitro* the substance seems incapable of binding antibody unless substances such as lecithin or cholesterol are present, and in this it is peculiar even among haptens. Geiduschek and Doty (1952) observed that Wasserman antibody would not adsorb to a monomolecular film of pure cardiolipin and that lecithin or cholesterol needed to be mixed with pure cardiolipin in such instances to bring about binding. Under such favorable circumstances, however, binding could be very specific for cardiolipin and very strong.

The surface properties of cardiolipin-lecithin mixtures not only favor the binding of antibody to cardiolipin; they also stabilize the aqueous retention of lecithin (Dawson and Bangham, 1959). Cardiolipin in small amounts prevents organic-solvent extraction of lecithin. Moreover, it activates the hydrolysis of lecithin by phospholipase B. Apparently it has the ability of changing the ζ-potential of lecithin from a net positive to a net negative value that is more favorable for enzyme binding. Conversely, then, one might suspect that the reason why lecithin enhances the binding of antibody to cardiolipin is that it reduces the high negative charge of the hapten. If so, then anti-cardiolipin antibody would in essence be directed against a hybrid hapten in Singer's full meaning of that term. This would not be surprising. In nature cardiolipin is highly absorbed, e.g., in mammalian mitochondria, and apparently participates heavily in electron transfer reactions of oxidative enzyme systems. As an immunogen it would be expected to be most active in a strongly bound state. This would be the way its haptenic properties could be expressed. But in such a strongly bound state its anionic nature would be considerably discharged and antibody would most likely form against the neutralized material.

Cardiolipin is unique among lipids in structure since it is, as Brady and Trams (1964) expressed it, "the only non-carbohydrate-containing lipid shown to possess strong haptenic properties." Not until 1947 was this fact brought out and made clear. In that year Pangborn presented a complete analysis of the beef heart lipid and even suggested a structure that was in accord with the values he had obtained since his initial report in 1942: four glycerol molecules linked by three phosphoric acid residues and esterified by five linoleic acid groups and one oleic acid. Faure and Coulon (1948) quickly confirmed Pangborn's analyses, but it took more time before Macfarlane and Gray (1957) finally were able to work out a much more suitable structural formula. This in turn brought into prominence a hitherto unrecognized but very widely distributed group of substances called the polyglycerophosphatides. Cardiolipin was then recognized as a diphosphatidylglycerol, bis-(diacyl-L-glyceryl-phosphoryl)glycerol. As Marfarlane (1964) pointed out, the name "cardiolipin" is "strictly only applicable to the unsaturated C_{18}-acid derivatives with a preponderance of linoleic acid, found in mammalian tissues."

$$R-CO-O-CH_2 \quad O \quad O-CH_2 \quad O \quad O-CH_2$$
$$R-CO-O-CH \quad \overset{\parallel}{P} \quad HO-CH \quad \overset{\parallel}{P} \quad HC-O-OC-R$$
$$H_2C-O \quad OH \quad H_2C-O \quad OH \quad H_2C-O-OC-R$$

Cardiolipin, a diphosphatidylglycerol

Benson and Strickland (1960) have identified similar polyglycerophosphates in plants, an explanation, as pointed out by Brady and Trams (1964) and described by Tribondeau (1913), of the cross-reactivity of plant extracts in the Wasserman reaction. Direct evidence of the surprising free hydroxyl in the central glycerol residue was obtained by Coulon-Morelec (as described by Faure and Coulon-Morelec, 1963), who was able to acetylate the compound under controlled conditions using acetic acid along with dicyclohexylcarbodiimide in a pyridine medium. Brady and Trams (1964) have remarked about the antigenicity of cardiolipin as follows:

> The haptenic property of cardiolipin is particularly intriguing since it seems to rule out the necessity for the presence of a carbohydrate residue as a portion of the immunologically active molecule. The principal question which requires exploration at this moment is whether there must be a free hydroxyl group on the central glycerol molecule.

On the basis of the free β-carbon hydroxyl group, Brady and Trams raised the question of whether some of the α-O-amino acid esters of phosphatidylglycerols, such as discovered by Macfarlane (1962) in *Clostridium welchii*, might not also be haptenic, for they also contained a free β-hydroxyl group.

4. Glycosphingolipids

The Forssman hapten is not quite so ubiquitous as cardiolipin but appears to be spread at random among various species (Forssman, 1930). Its presence in guinea pigs and horses but absence in rabbits and rats, for example, confers upon it the tag of a heterophile antigen. The classic experiment performed by Forssman (1911) still may be regarded as typical and definitive—immunization of rabbits with guinea pig tissue to form antibodies that would cause lysis of sheep red cells in the presence of complement.

Forssman hapten may be regarded as a group of compounds rather than a single moiety. Papirmeister and Mallette (1955) have suggested that a typical member is composed of N-acylsphingosine, galactose, and N-acetylgalactosamine. But for Forssman hapten to be water-soluble, as it apparently is, Graf and Rapport (1960) argue that it cannot be such a simple molecule, and Brady and Trams (1964) agree. It is quite likely that the determinant groups are constructed as Papirmeister and Mallette suggest, but that in nature they are bound to a more complete residue. In fact, Brady and Trams raise the interesting possibility that Forssman haptens may after all be a heterogeneous collection of degradation products of erythrocytic globosides. These latter, described by Yamakawa, Yokoyama, and Kiso (1962) and Yamakawa, Yokoyama, and Handa (1963), can be written as N-acetylgalactosaminoyl-(1 → 6)-galactosyl-(1 → 4)-galactosyl-(1 → 4)-glucosylceramide. (The ceramide is another way of designating N-acylsphingosine.) Work such as that of Diehl and Mallette (1964) on the nature of Forssman hapten from sheep erythrocytes should soon provide answers to the questions raised.

Cytolipin H obtained by Rapport, Graf, and their colleagues from human tumor tissue and from bovine spleen turned out to be a glycosphingolipid with a structural formula suggestive of cerebronylsphingosylglucosidogalactoside, a ceramide lactoside (Rapport, Graf, and Yariv, 1961). Shapiro and Rachaman (1964) synthesized N-lignoceroyl-1-D-sphingosyl-β-lactoside, which was found by Rapport and Graf (1964) to be virtually indistinguishable in immunochemical properties from naturally occurring cytolipin H. Graf, Yariv, and Rapport (1965), by showing that anti-lactose antibodies were somewhat more specific for the lactoside structure of the cytolipin than were anti-cytolipin H antibodies, said in effect that although a good share of the immunological specificity of cytolipin H was due to its carbohydrate residues, the presence of the ceramide structure during antibody biosynthesis did have some influence. It was therefore of even greater importance, in identifying the natural with the synthetic cytolipin H compound, that the two reacted so similarly not only with anti-lactose antibodies but also with the more specific anti-cytolipin H antibodies.

Several other members of the cytolipin class have been isolated and identified, prominent among them being cytolipin K (Rapport, Graf, and Schneider, 1964) and brain galactocerebroside (Joffe, Rapport, and Graf, 1963; Rapport, Graf, Autilio, and Norton, 1964). Cytolipin K was found to be a ceramide complexed with glucose, galactose, and galactosamine. It was immunochemically distinct from Forssman, cardiolipin, cytolipins G and H, and the brain galactocerebroside.

Another class of glycosphingolipids that have recently become recognized as important naturally occurring substances are the gangliosides. As constituents of neuronal membranes, they contain N-acetylneuraminic acid residues attached to a backbone of ceramide-glucose-galactose-N-acetylgalactosamine-galactose (Brady and Trams, 1964). Antibodies against the gangliosides could be produced in rabbits if the glycolipids were absorbed to carriers such as rabbit red cells, and could be detected by hemagglutination of the antigen-coated red cells (Yokoyama, Trams, and Brady, 1963). The sialic acid residues were found to be most antigenic, and to be responsible for such effects as ganglioside inhibition of anti-M and anti-N agglutinations of human red cells. Sherwin, Lowden, and Wolfe (1964) were able to improve antibody production against these glycolipids and to improve the titers, thus making possible even better antibody reagents for continued study.

Asialogangliosides were also found to be antigenic when absorbed to red cells, and antibodies, non-cross-reactive with intact gangliosides, were produced (Yokoyama *et al.*, 1963). These antibodies were also non-cross-reactive with certain globosides but did cross-react with some glycosphingolipids containing ceramide, glucose, galactose, and N-acetylgalactosamine (Somers, Kanfer, Brady, and Boone, 1964). An intensive study of the differences in reactivity among the asialoganglioside, cytolipin, and Forssman haptens should bring about a resolution of structural differences, mainly in the sequence of carbohydrate residues, that create the observed specificities. With the sialic-acid containing glycosphingolipids, immunochemical reactions may be expected to be more associated with sialic acid determinants than with the glycosphingolipids *per se;* and the cross-reactions, more with other structures that also contain the N-acetylneuraminic acid groups.

Rapport (1961) summarized the problems involved in glycosphingolipid immunochemistry in this way:

> It may be concluded that potential antigenicity is an inherent property of glycosphingolipids and that the manifestation of this property in each phase of immunological activity requires auxiliary lipids. From the standpoint of pathological processes, efforts to establish the possible involvement of immune mechanisms require detection of antibody, and, in turn, detection of antibody is dependent on the nature of the test antigen. An understanding of the possible role of glycosphingolipids as potential autoantigens will require much sophisticated investigation on the relation of structure to antigenicity and the manner in which antigenicity in its various phases is affected by lipid-lipid interactions.

The experience of Kościelak (1963) with two blood group A-specific glycolipids is evidence of the type of sophistication that is required. Both lipids were obtained from human erythrocytes, both were found to contain galactosamine, glucosamine, galactose, glucose, sialic acid, fucose, and sphingosine, and both were equally active in quantitative precipitation analyses. They differed in fatty acid residues and in solubility. One was insoluble in cold methanol, the other was soluble. They also differed in their ability to inhibit hemagglutination. The methanol-insoluble lipid was 100 times more active in this way than the methanol-soluble lipid, but the latter could be rendered as active as the former if mixed with auxiliary lipid; on the other hand, if the two were mixed together the activity was low and close to that of the methanol-soluble lipid. Kościelak concluded in a cautionary way that the immunochemical activity of bloodgroup substances extracted from red cells may depend to a large extent upon their state of aggregation in aqueous solution.

5. Teichoic acids and mucopeptides

Through modern advances in the separation of substances from cells, a number of new products have been isolated. Among these are the teichoic acids. One group has a polymeric glycerophosphate backbone and the other a polyribitol phosphate form. Both contain glycosidically linked sugars and esterified D-alanine. The intracellular D-antigens of Group D streptococci are representative of the glycerol group (Wicken and Baddiley, 1963) while the cell wall antigens of *Staphylococcus aureus* contain the ribitol type (Armstrong, Baddiley, Buchanan, and Carss, 1958; Sanderson, Juergens, and Strominger, 1961). According to McCarty (1964) the ester-linked D-alanine is an important determinant in the specificity of Group A streptococci, suppressing, so to speak, the reactivity of underlying glycerophosphate residues; in the case of *S. aureus*, the α-N-acetylglucosaminylribitol appears to predominate (Sanderson *et al.*, 1961; Baddiley, Buchanan, Rajbhandary, and Sanderson, 1962). In all instances the sugar residues appear to be antigenic, such as kojibiose, an α-D-glucose $(1 \rightarrow 2)$-D-glucose, in Strain 39 Group D streptococci, and kojitriose in Strain 8191 (Wicken, Elliott, and Baddiley, 1963; Wicken and Baddiley, 1963; Elliott, 1962).

Another constituent of the bacterial cell wall, the mucopeptide component, had long been recognized as essential for the rigid structure of the cell wall, but had never been seriously implicated as a natural bacterial antigen. Now Abdulla and Schwab (1965) have shown that not even this structure, the most ubiquitous type of substance in the bacterial field, can be left out of the antigenic compilation. Because of the ease with which quantitative aggregation reactions can be carried out between such material and antibody, it is certain to become another useful substance for detailed immunochemical analysis.

6. Nucleic acids

Evidence that purine determinants were involved in the appearance of anti-DNA antibodies in lupus erythematosus serum was given by Stollar and Levine (1963). It was noted that denatured but not native DNA would react with the antibodies and that the reaction was inhibited by purine derivatives. Using synthesized polyfunctional antigens containing uracil and 5-acetyluracil residues, Tanenbaum and Beiser (1963) obtained rabbit antibodies that would also cross-react much more strongly with denatured DNA than with the so-called native product. Extending the work still further, Erlanger and Beiser (1964) found that antibodies to nucleosides and nucleotides (conjugated to BSA) would react with thermally denatured DNA but not ribonucleic acid (RNA). Plescia, Braun, and Palczuk (1964) conferred antigenic properties upon thermally denatured calf thymus DNA and T4 phage DNA by complexing them with methylated BSA and found specific differences in immunological reactivity between the two DNA products with little cross-reactivity. Sela, Ungar-Waron, and Shechter (1964) synthesized multichain polypeptides containing uridine-5'-carboxylic acid residues, produced anti-uridine antibodies in rabbits against the material, and found that the antibodies reacted with both thermally denatured RNA and DNA, as well as polyuridylic acid, but not polyadenylic acid, native *Escherichia coli* RNA, or double-stranded calf-thymus DNA.

One of the problems in working with cross-reactions of antibodies with denatured DNA and RNA had been the lack of precipitability, necessitating complement fixation and other indirect tests to determine binding. As a result of the work of Beiser, Tanenbaum, and Erlanger (1964), however, precipitation reactions were worked out and specificities more easily determined. The authors concluded on a hopeful note, suggesting that antibody reactivity and purine-pyrimidine base sequence might be obtainable and, if so, that an exquisite technique for investigating the subtle substructures of nucleic acids would be at hand.

7. Steroid-hormone conjugates

A number of studies on antibodies to steroid haptens have been made since Erlanger, Borek, Beiser, and Lieberman (1957) attached testosterone to BSA and immunized laboratory animals with it. To indicate the specificity obtainable, the neutralization of the hormonal effects *in vivo* by antibodies has been obtained against testosterone, estrone, cortisol, and aldosterone (Neri, Rolksdorf, Beiser, Erlanger, Agate, and Lieberman, 1964).

REFERENCES

Abdulla, E. M., and Schwab, J. H. (1965). Immunological properties of bacterial cell wall mucopeptides. Proc. Soc. Exptl. Biol. Med. *118:* 359–362.

Armstrong, J., Baddiley, J., Buchanan, J. G., and Carss, B. (1958). Nucleotides and the bacterial cell wall. Nature *181:* 1692–1693.

Baddiley, J., Buchanan, J. G., Rajbhandary, U. L., and Sanderson, A. R. (1962). Teichoic acid from the walls of *Staphylococcus aureus* (H). Structure of the *N*-acetylglucosaminylribitol residues. Biochem. J. *82:* 439–448.

Beiser, S. M., Tanenbaum, S. W., and Erlanger, B. F. (1964). Purine- and pyrimidine-specific antibodies: precipitation with denatured deoxyribonucleic acid. Nature *203:* 1381–1382.

Benson, A. A., and Strickland, E. H. (1960). Plant phospholipids. III. Identification of diphosphatidyl glycerol. Biochim. Biophys. Acta *41:* 328–333.

Brady, R. O., and Trams, E. G. (1964). The chemistry of lipids. Ann. Rev. Biochem. *33:* 75–100.

Buchanan-Davidson, D., Stahmann, M., and Dellert, E. (1959). Immunochemistry of synthetic polypeptides and polypeptidyl proteins. IV. Immunologic reactions of the synthetic polypeptides. J. Immunol. *83:* 561–570.

Dawson, R. M. C., and Bangham, A. D. (1959). The activation of surface films of lecithin by amphipathic molecules. Biochem. J. *72:* 493–496.

Detre, L. (1906). Ueber den Nachweis von spezifischen Syphilis-antisubstanzen und deren Antigenen bei Luetikern. Wien. Klin. Wochschr. *19:* 619–620.

Diehl, J. E., and Mallette, M. F. (1964). Nature of the Forssman hapten from sheep erythrocytes. J. Immunol. *93:* 965–971.

Elliott, S. D. (1962). Teichoic acid and the group antigen of group D streptococci. Nature *193:* 1105–1106.

Erlanger, B., and Beiser, S. (1964). Antibodies specific for ribonucleosides and ribonucleotides and their reaction with DNA. Proc. Natl. Acad. Sci. U. S. *52:* 68–74.

Erlanger, B. F., Borek, F., Beiser, S. M., and Lieberman, S. (1957). Steroid-protein conjugates. I. Preparation and characterization of conjugates of bovine serum albumin with testosterone and with cortisone. J. Biol. Chem. *228:* 713–727.

Faure, M., and Coulon, M.-J. (1948). Les phosphatides du muscle cardiaque. Préparation des acides phosphatidiques. Bull. Soc. Chim. Biol. *30:* 533–538.

Faure, M., and Coulon-Morelec, M.-J. (1963). Rapports entre la structure chimique du cardiolipide et son activité serologique. Conservation du cardiolipide. Ann. Inst. Pasteur *104:* 246–263.

Forssman, J. (1911). Die Herstellung hochwertiger spezifischer Schafhämolysine ohne Verwendung von Schafblut. Ein Beitrag zur Lehre von heterologer Antikörperbildung. Biochem. Z. *37:* 78–115.

Forssman, J. (1930). Die heterogenetischen Antigene, besonders die sog. Forssman-Antigene und ihre Antikörper. Kolle and Wassermann's Handbuch der pathogenen Micro-organismen, 3rd Ed., Vol. 3, Part 1 (G. Fischer, Jena, 828 pp.), pp. 469–526.

Fuchs, S., and Sela, M. (1963). Studies of the chemical basis of the antigenicity of proteins. 6. Antigenic specificity of some synthetic polypeptides containing tyrosine. Biochem. J. *87:* 70–79.

Geiduschek, P., and Doty, P. (1952). A surface-chemical study of a hapten-antibody reaction: The reaction of a Wasserman antibody. J. Am. Chem. Soc. *74:* 3110–3115.

Gill, T. H., and Doty, P. (1960). A strongly antigenic synthetic polypeptide. J. Mol. Biol. *2:* 65–68.

Gould, H. J., Gill, T. J., III, and Kunz, H. W. (1964). Studies on synthetic polypeptide antigens. XII. The effects of pH, ionic strength, temperature, and nonaqueous solvents on antibody activity and the antibody-synthetic polypeptide interaction. J. Biol. Chem. *239:* 3071–3082.

Graf, L., and Rapport, M. M. (1960). Immunochemical studies of organ and tumor lipids. VII. The reactivity of anti-human tumor sera with cytolipin H, cardiolipin, and Forssman haptens. Cancer Res. *20:* 546–550.

Graf, L., Yariv, J., and Rapport, M. M. (1965). Immunochemical studies of organ and tumor lipids. XV. The reactivity of anti-lactose sera with cytolipin H. Immunochemistry *2:* 145–153.

Hooker, S. B., and Boyd, W. C. (1934). The existence of antigenic determinants of diverse specificity in a single protein. II. In two natural proteins: crystalline duck egg albumin and crystalline hen egg albumin. J. Immunol. *26:* 460–479.

Joffe, S., Rapport, M. M., and Graf, L. (1963). Identification of an organ specific lipid hapten in brain. Nature *197:* 60–62.

Kaminski, M. (1962). Immunochemical studies on human siderophilin. Nature *194:* 27–28.

Korngold, L. (1963). Antigenic differences among human haptoglobins. Intern. Arch. Allergy Appl. Immunol. *23:* 268–280.

Kościelak, J. (1963). Blood group specific glycolipids from human erythrocytes. Biochim. Biophys. Acta *78:* 313–328.

Landsteiner, K., Müller, R., and Pötzl, O. (1907). Zur Frage der Komplement bindungs reaktionen bei Syphilis. Wien. Klin. Wochschr. *20:* 1565–1567.

Landsteiner, K., and van der Scheer, J. (1940). On cross reactions of egg albumin sera. J. Exptl. Med. *71:* 445–454.

Lapresle, C. and Webb, T. (1965). Isolation and study of a fragment of human serum albumin containing one of the antigenic sites of the whole molecule. Biochem. J. *95:* 245–251.

Macfarlane, M. G. (1962). Characterization of lipoamino acids as O-amino-acid esters of phosphatidyl-glycerol. Nature *196:* 136–138.

Macfarlane, M. G. (1964). Phosphatidylglycerols and lipoamino acids. Advan. Lipid Res. *2:* 91–125.

Macfarlane, M. G., and Gray, G. M. (1957). Composition of cardiolipin. Bioc em. J. *67:* 25p–26p.

Maurer, P. H., (1962). Antigenicity of polypeptides (poly-α-amino acids). II. J. Immunol. *88:* 330–338.

Maurer, P. H. (1963). Antigenicity of polypeptides (poly-*alpha*-amino acids). X. Studies with polymers of *D*-amino acids. Proc. Soc. Exptl. Biol. Med. *113:* 553–557.

Maurer, P., Gerulat, B. F., and Pinchuck, P. (1964). Antigenicity of polypeptides (poly-α-amino acids). XI. Quantitative relationships among polymers and rabbit antisera. J. Biol. Chem. *239:* 922–929.

McCarty, M. (1964). The role of D-alanine in the serological specificity of group A streptococcal glycerol teichoic acid. Proc. Natl. Acad. Sci. U. S. *52:* 259–265.

Metzger, H., Sharp, G. C., and Edelhoch, H. (1962). The properties of thyroglobulin. VII. The immunologic activity of thyroglobulin fragments. Biochemistry *1*: 205–214.

Michaelis, L. (1907). Die Wasserman'sche Syphilis reaktion. Berlin Klin. Wochschr. *44*: 1103–1107.

Miller, H., and Feeney, R. (1964). Immunochemical relationships of proteins of avian egg whites. Arch. Biochem. Biophys. *108*: 117–124.

Morton, J., and Deutsch, H. F. (1961). Immunochemical studies of modified ovomucoids. Arch. Biochem. Biophys. *93*: 661–665.

Neri, R. O., Rolksdorf, S., Beiser, S. M., Erlanger, B. F., Agate, F. J., Jr., and Lieberman, S. (1964). Further studies on the biological effects of passive immunization with antibodies to steroid-protein conjugates. Endocrinology *74*: 493–599.

Ovary, Z. (1964). Antigenicity of hemoglobin and its constituents. I. Antigenicity of human adult hemoglobin and its structural units (*alpha* and *beta* chains). Immunochemistry *1*: 241–248.

Pangborn, M. C. (1942). Isolation and purification of a serologically active phospholipid from beef heart. J. Biol. Chem. *143*: 247–256.

Pangborn, M. C. (1947). The composition of cardiolipin. J. Biol. Chem. *168*: 351–361.

Papirmeister, B., and Mallette, M. F. (1955). The isolation and some properties of the Forssman hapten from sheep erythrocytes. Arch. Biochem. Biophys. *57*: 94–105.

Plescia, O. J., Braun, W., and Palczuk, N. C. (1964). Production of antibodies to denatured deoxyribonucleic acid (DNA). Proc. Natl. Acad. Sci. U. S. *52*: 279–285.

Ram, J. S., and Maurer, P. H. (1958). Modified bovine serum albumin. IV. Characterization and immunochemical studies of the O-acetylated derivative. Arch. Biochem. Biophys. *74*: 119–130.

Rangel, H. (1965). Study of cross-reaction between rabbit anti-bovine serum albumin antibodies and equine serum albumin. Immunology *8*: 88–94.

Rapport, M. M. (1961). The antigenic properties of sphingolipids. Proc. Neurochem. Symp. Rome, pp. 83–89.

Rapport, M. M., and Graf, L. (1964). Serological activity of cytolipin H (lactocytoside). Nature *201*: 879–880.

Rapport, M. M., Graf, L., Autilio, L. A., and Norton, W. T. (1964). Immunochemical studies of organ and tumor lipids. XIV. Galactocerebroside determinants in the myelin sheath of the central nervous system. J. Neurochem. *11*: 855–864.

Rapport, M. M., Graf, L., and Schneider, H. (1964). Immunochemical studies of organ and tumor lipids. XIII. Isolation of cytolipin K, a glycosphingolipid hapten present in human kidney. Arch. Biochem. Biophys. *105*: 431–438.

Rapport, M. M., Graf, L., and Yariv, J. (1961). Immunochemical studies of organ and tumor lipids. IX. Configuration of the carbohydrate residues in cytolipin H. Arch. Biochem. Biophys. *92*: 438–440.

Rejnek, J., Bednarik, T., and Koci, J. (1963). Microheterogeneity of albumin. Clin. Chim. Acta *8*: 116–126.

Sanderson, A. R., Juergens, W. G., and Strominger, J. L. (1961). Chemical and immunochemical structure of teichoic acid from Staphylococcus aureus (Copenhagen). Biochem. Biophys. Res. Commun. *5*: 472–476.

Sela, M., Ungar-Waron, H., and Shechter, Y. (1964). Uridine-specific antibodies obtained with synthetic antigens. Proc. Natl. Acad. Sci. U. S. *52:* 285–292.

Shapiro, D., and Rachaman, E. (1964). Total synthesis of cytolipin H. Nature *201:* 878–879.

Sherwin, A. L., Lowden, J. A., and Wolfe, L. S. (1964). The production of antisera to gangliosides from human nervous tissue. Can. J. Biochem. *42:* 1640–1643.

Somers, J. E., Kanfer, J. N., Brady, R. O., and Boone, J. M. (1964). Immunochemical studies with gangliosides. II. Investigations of the structure of gangliosides by the hapten-inhibition technique. Biochemistry *3:* 251–254.

Stollar, D., and Levine, L. (1963). Antibodies to denatured deoxyribonucleic acid in lupus erythematosus serum. IV. Evidence for purine determinants in DNA. Arch. Biochem. Biophys. *101:* 417–422.

Tanenbaum, S. W., and Beiser, S. M. (1963). Pyrimidine-specific antibodies which react with deoxyribonucleic acid (DNA). Proc. Natl. Acad. Sci. U. S. *49:* 662–668.

Tribondeau, L. (1913). Emploi d'extraits végétaux dans la réaction de Wasserman. Compt. Rend. *156:* 340–342.

Weigle, W. O. (1961). Immunochemical properties of the cross-reactions between anti-BSA and heterologous albumins. J. Immunol. *87:* 599–607.

Wicken, A. J., and Baddiley, J. (1963). Structure of intracellular teichoic acids from group D streptococci. Biochem. J. *87:* 54–62.

Wicken, A. J., Elliott, S. D., and Baddiley, J. (1963). The identity of streptococcal group D antigen with teichoic acid. J. Gen. Microbiol. *31:* 231–239.

Yamakawa, T., Yokoyama, S., and Handa, N. (1963). Chemistry of lipids of post-hemolytic residue or stroma of erythrocytes. XI. Structure of globoside, the main mucolipid of human erythrocytes. J. Biochem. (Tokyo) *52:* 228–229.

Yamakawa, T., Yokoyama, S., and Kiso, N. (1962). Structure of main globoside of human erythrocytes. J. Biochem. (Tokyo) *53:* 28–36.

Yokoyama, M., Trams, E. G., and Brady, R. O. (1963). Immunochemical studies with gangliosides. J. Immunol. *90:* 372–380.

Glossary of Abbreviations

A, Ig heavy chain
a, heterogeneity index
Ab, antibody
Ag, antigen
Ala, alanine
Ap, phenyltrimethylammonium
Apz, p-azophenyltrimethylammonium ion

B, Ig light chain
BGG, bovine immuno-γ-globulin
BPO, benzylpenicilloyl
BSA, bovine serum albumin

CM-cellulose, carboxymethyl-cellulose

DAA, diazoacetamide
DCC, N,N′dicyclohexylcarbodiimide
DEAE-cellulose, diethylaminoethyl-cellulose
DHNDS, 4,5-dihydroxy-3-(p-nitrophenylazo)-2,7-naphthalenedisul-
 fonic acid disodium salt
DNA, deoxyribonucleic acid
DNP, din·trophenyl

EA, egg albumin

F, antigen valence
Fab, IgG fragment from papain digest with Ab activity
Fc, crystalline IgG fragment from papain digest
Fd, heavy chain piece in Fab
F-fragment, electrophoretically fast fragment, mouse IgG
FO, fluorescein-ovalbumin

G, m-aminobenzylglycine
GIL, sym-aminoisophthalyl-glycine-leucine
Glu, glutamic acid
Gly, glycine
Gm, allotypic determinants on Fc fragment of human IgG

H chain, heavy chain of Ig
His, histidine
HSA, human serum albumin

Ig, immunoglobulin
InV, allotypic determinants on L chain of human Ig
Ip, phenyl-(*p*-aminobenzoylamino)acetic acid

L, *m*-aminobenzoylleucine
Lac, *p*-azophenyl-β-lactoside
L chain, light chain of Ig
Leu, leucine
Lys, lysine

N, Ab nitrogen in Heidelberger-Kendall equation
NP, *p*-nitrophenyl

Ov, ovalbumin (egg albumin)

PAB-cellulose, *p*-aminobenzyl cellulose
PCA, passive cutaneous anaphylaxis
Ps, pneumococcal polysaccharide

RNA, ribonucleic acid
Rp, benzenearsonate, phenylarsonate (sometimes **R**)
Rpz, *p*-azobenzenearsonate, *p*-azophenylarsonate
Rpz-FB, *p*-(arsonic acid)-benzenediazonium fluoborate

S, amount of polysaccharide in Heidelberger-Kendall equation
S, in S-I, S-II, S-III, etc., type-specific pneumococcal polysaccharide
S, in 3.5S, 7S, 19S, etc., sedimentation coefficient in Svedberg units
S-fragment, electrophoretically slow fragment, mouse IgG
S—S, disulfide bond

Tyr, tyrosine

Xp, benzoate (sometimes **X**)
Xpa, *p*-aminobenzoate
Xpi, *p*-iodobenzoate
Xpz, *p*-azobenzoate

POSTSCRIPT

My motivations for writing these chapters have not been entirely the selfless ones of promoting the subject of immunochemistry nor solely those of providing my students with a systematic series of lectures on immunochemistry. Much more to the point, I had arrived at a crucial stage in my own current research that required a critical examination of where I was, where I should go, and where, for that matter, I had been.

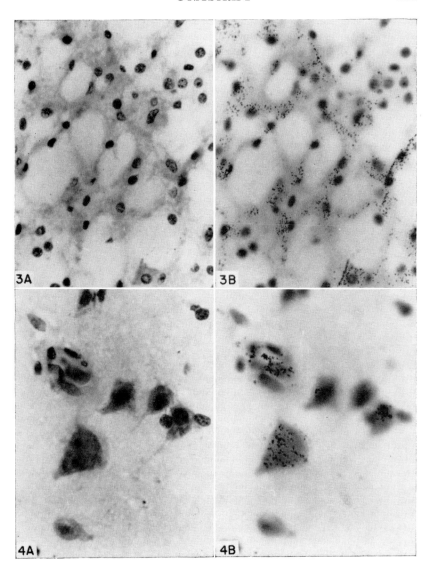

FIG. 34. Radioautograph of *in vivo* localized ^{125}I-labeled antibody in a biopsied human brain tumor. (Mahaley, Mahaley, and Day, 1965.)

My main goal in research had been for over a decade to understand the process of tissue-localization of radioactive antibodies *in vivo* well enough to exploit the technique as a means of carrying diagnostic and therapeutic amounts of radioactivity specifically to cancer sites. The knowledge and experience gained through daily laboratory work during that period was enough to convince me that the endeavor was certainly not a hopeless one; however, it also became suddenly clear that a broader view and a different perspective were needed before I could go much further. I was confronted with three main problems:

Specific radioantibody localization in cancer depended upon: (1) delivery of radioantibodies to cancer sites via vascular channels leading to and from the malignant tissues; (2) the presence of distinctive antigens in cancer tissues that would be foci for radioantibody absorption; and (3) the purification of monospecific antibodies that would act as specific carriers of the radioactive isotopes, that would not cross-react with normal tissues, and that would not non-specifically remain in the circulation.

The re-examination of the first problem resulted in the progress report, *Vascular Relationships of Tumor and Host* (Day, 1964); consideration of the second problem led to attempts to place the question of specific cancer antigens in proper perspective, and led to the monograph, *The Immunochemistry of Cancer* (Day, 1965); probing the third problem took me through the material that has formed the subject matter of *Foundations of Immunochemistry*, the structure and reactivity of antibody re-reagents.

It is now time to return to the laboratory and make use of this greater understanding and broadened perspective in another decade of work. Figure 34 is symbolic of the job ahead, a radioautograph of a semi-purified form of ^{125}I-labeled antibody that has localized *in vivo* in a human brain tumor (Day, Lassiter, Woodhall, Mahaley, and Mahaley, 1965; Mahaley, Mahaley, and Day, 1965; Day, Lassiter, and Mahaley, 1965). The antibody is present typically in a concentration of less than 0.0001 microgram per gram of tissue. Our job: to recover the antibody and test for specificity; isolate and identify the antigens responsible for localization of the specific antibody portion; immunize laboratory animals with the isolated antigens in order, hopefully, to obtain specific antibody in larger quantities; purify the antibody still further through the use of purified antigens; and, finally, to label the purified product with enough radioactivity to turn it into an effective diagnostic and therapeutic tool. There is little doubt that the problems posed in this project could easily cover the range of immunochemistry; there is also little doubt that success will depend upon such coverage.

—E.D.D.

October 8, 1965

REFERENCES

Day, E. A. (1964). Vascular relationships of tumor and host. Prog. experimental Tumor Res. *4:* 57–97.

Day, E. D. (1965). *The Immunochemistry of Cancer.* Charles C Thomas (Springfield, 170 pp.).

Day, E. D., Lassiter, S., Woodhall, B., Mahaley, J., and Mahaley, M. S., Jr. (1965). The localization of radioantibodies in human brain tumors. I. Preliminary exploration. Cancer Res. *25:* 773–778.

Mahaley, M. S., Jr., Mahaley, J., and Day, E. D. (1965). The localization of radioantibodies in human brain tumors. II. Radioautography. Cancer Res. *25:* 779–793.

Day, E. D., Lassiter, S., and Mahaley, M. S., Jr. (1965). The localization of radioantibodies in human brain tumors. III. Radioiodination of pre-purified localizing antibody. J. Nuclear Med. *6:* 38–52.

Author Index

193

Subject Index